Unity within diversity

4

Photos on title page Three members of the tit family: (top) blue tit (*Parus caeruleus*), (middle) great tit (*P. major*) and (bottom) coal tit (*P. ater*). They have many features in common (unity), but can also be distinguished in a variety of ways.

The Open University, Walton Hall, Milton Keynes MK7 6AA

First published 1998

Written, edited, designed and typeset by The Open University.

Printed and bound in the United Kingdom by Jarrold Book Printing, Norfolk, England.

ISBN 0 7492 8190 1

This text forms part of an Open University course, S103 *Discovering Science*. The complete list of texts that make up this course can be found on the back cover. Details of this and other Open University courses can be obtained from the Course Reservations and Sales Office, PO Box 724, The Open University, Milton Keynes MK7 6ZS, United Kingdom: tel. (00 44) 1908 653231.

For availability of this or other course components, contact Open University Worldwide Ltd, The Berrill Building, Walton Hall, Milton Keynes MK7 6AA, United Kingdom: tel. (00 44) 1908 858585, fax (00 44) 1908 858787, e-mail ouwenq@open.ac.uk

Alternatively, much useful course information can be obtained from the Open University's website: http://www.open.ac.uk

s103block4i1.1

Contents

Introduction

1

The final section of Block 3 was concerned with the biosphere, that part of the Earth which is capable of supporting life. As a stage on our journey in the first half of *Discovering Science* from the very large (galaxies and the Solar System) to the very small, we turn our attention in this block to the living organisms which inhabit the biosphere.

At any one time, a huge number of individual organisms are to be found living somewhere on our planet. These organisms come in millions of different types, or species. By definition, each species is different from every other species. Moreover, you will know from everyday experience that individual organisms within a species (such as humans) differ from one other.

Thus, when we start to look in detail at the inhabitants of the biosphere we immediately become aware of the immense *diversity* they display. So how can we make sense of all this diversity? Fortunately, there is fundamental *unity* underlying the diversity. This block looks at living organisms (the science of biology) in the context of unity on the one hand and diversity on the other.

We start in Section 2 by trying to answer the deceptively simple question 'what is life?' and find that all living organisms share just three particular processes or attributes of life. Further unity is provided by the organization of living material into microscopic units called cells (Section 3). We next turn our attention to the other side of the coin — diversity — and look at how species are defined, labelled and classified (Section 4), and the extent and significance of biodiversity, the loss of which is of major current concern (Section 5).

Reproduction (Section 6) is one of the three attributes of life. How and when it is achieved is crucial to the life histories of different species. We look at the life histories of several interacting species in Section 7, which explores energy flow through the organisms within an oak wood ecosystem. In Section 8 we look at some of the factors which influence the size of populations of organisms. Here you will start some field work (to be completed when you study Block 9) on the population dynamics of a particular species, a small fly called the holly leaf miner.

The adaptation of organisms to their environment was touched on briefly in Block 2. Section 9 studies one of the most famous examples of adaptation — that of the finches which Charles Darwin found on the Galapagos Islands. Mention of Darwin brings us to *the* most significant unifying concept in the whole of biology: evolution. Sections 10 and 11 are concerned with how evolution is brought about by natural selection. The block ends with a brief Section 12, in which we reflect on different levels of explanation in biology, from whole ecological systems down to interacting molecules; the existence of different levels of explanation should be borne in mind as you continue your exploration of the science of living organisms.

Given the tremendous diversity of living organisms, it is perhaps not surprising that one of the skills given particular emphasis in this block is the classification of scientific information by recognizing essential unifying features. Biology is a branch of science that is relatively rich in technical terms. Another skill emphasized in this block is therefore how to remember the meanings of the most significant of those terms. This block should also help you develop your communication skills using these technical terms, and also the ability to use diagrams for communicating science.

Activity 1.1 Planning ahead

Before you get to grips with the main part of the block, take a few minutes to think ahead about how you will study it, particularly about how you will fit in the time for the two long CD-ROM activities and for completion of the assignment questions for this block. ◄

What is life?

2

Look around any garden or park and it is easy to pick out the living from the non-living (Figure 2.1). The hedge, the trees, the flowers, the birds and the people are living, whereas the seats and tables and the fountain are non-living. To answer the question 'what is life?' should simply be a matter of listing those things, those qualities, that living things share with each other, but which they do not share with non-living things. Unfortunately, such a list is not easy to compile, as you would discover quickly if you tried to specify what flowers, humans and birds have in common.

Figure 2.1   Queen's Court in Central Milton Keynes.

There are, however, three qualities that these organisms, and all other organisms, do share. They form the subject matter for this section, and indeed for much of biology.

The qualities possessed by all living organisms are *reproduction*, *growth* and *metabolism*. These three shared qualities are called **attributes of life**.

2.1   Life arises from the living

Before you go on holiday, it is always a good idea to empty your teapot (and coffee cup and fruit bowl). If you do not, then when you return you will find a fine cottony mat of material growing on the tea (or coffee or fruit). The material will be floating on the surface of the tea and it will probably be white with flecks of black (although different types have different colours, including green and orange). If you are away for only a few days, then the cottony mat will scarcely be visible; but if you are away for a week or two, the mat will be very conspicuous. The material arises from organisms (known as moulds or *fungi,* singular: *fungus*) growing on the tea. Figure 2.2 shows a fungus growing on the surface of a carrot.

Figure 2.2 Close-up of a fungus (*Rhizopus stolonifer*) growing on a carrot (magnification about ×10). *Rhizopus stolonifer* is the scientific label of this particular fungus. Scientific labels were introduced in Section 11 of Block 3, and their use is explained in Section 4 of this block.

○ What quality of fungi suggests that they are living organisms?

○ The quality that suggests that fungi are living organisms is growth; the longer you are away on holiday, the bigger they get.

The observation that they apparently appear from nothing raises the question 'where do fungi come from?'.

You may well know the answer, but the question provoked considerable debate during the 19th century. There were those scientists, championed by Félix-Archimède Pouchet, who thought that the fungus arose from whatever it grew on, e.g. from within the tea or the rotting fruit. Such scientists accepted that fungi would be created over and over again, without parents, provided only that the conditions were right, i.e. wherever it was warm and damp and there was something for them grow on (e.g. tea, fruit or bread). Therefore, as fungi are living organisms, they also accepted that life could be repeatedly created. Pouchet and like-minded scientists supported the theory of *spontaneous generation*, the idea that certain forms of life could arise spontaneously.

Other scientists disagreed. They could not accept that life was being created over and over again. Instead they supported the theory that fungi arose from minute fungal particles carried in the air. These particles eventually settled onto surfaces and, if those surfaces were suitable (e.g. tea or bread), then the fungal particles would begin to grow and produce visible fungus. These scientists supported the view that life arose only from material that was already living; in other words, spontaneous generation did not occur.

The argument in favour of the small airborne particle hypothesis was clinched in 1867 by another French scientist, Louis Pasteur (Figure 2.3). Pasteur conducted a meticulous series of experiments which led him to the final, conclusive experiment described here. He believed that the fungi which grew on suitable surfaces must either have been present already, or had arrived there from the air. He therefore devised an experiment that did two things. First, fungi had to be eliminated from the suitable surface before starting the experiment. Second, it was necessary to prevent any new fungal particles arriving on the surface from the air. Under these very specific conditions in which no fungal particles were present, no fungi should grow on the surface.

Figure 2.3 Louis Pasteur (1822–1895), after whom the process of pasteurization is named.

⬤ What would it mean if fungi did grow on the surface under these conditions?

○ It would mean that spontaneous generation did occur.

Pasteur decided to use a liquid (a solution of sugar in water plus a small amount of brewers' waste) rather than a solid, because he knew from previous experiments that the liquid could support fungal growth but that boiling it would eliminate any fungal particles present. To prevent particles settling onto the mixture from the air, he devised a special flask, the neck of which he could stretch and bend into a long thin 'U' after the mixture had been put into the flask (Figure 2.4). He reasoned that the thin neck would allow air to be in contact with the mixture, but would reduce the movement of air, so that any fungal particles in the air would be trapped in the bottom of the 'U'.

Pasteur found that fungus did not grow on or within the solution; it remained clear of life. This seemed to indicate that when life was eliminated from the solution and the air above it, nothing would grow in the solution. But there is another reason why nothing might grow.

⬤ What other possible reason could there be for nothing growing in the solution?

○ The conditions in the flask may no longer be suitable for fungal growth.

⬤ How could the conditions in the flask be tested for their suitability for fungal growth?

○ Some fungal particles could be introduced to see if they can grow.

Pasteur introduced fungal particles by tipping the flask so that some of the solution ran down into the 'U' and then tipping it back into the body of the flask (Figure 2.5). By doing this he was also hoping to prove that living particles were indeed trapped in the 'U'. As a consequence of the tipping, fungus grew in the solution.

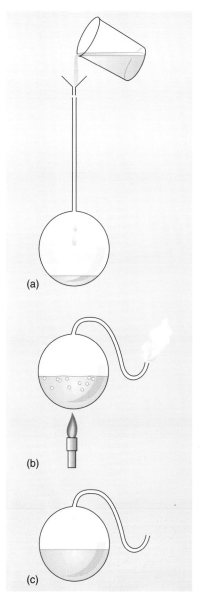

Figure 2.4 Pasteur's conclusive experiment. (a) The sugar solution is introduced to the flask. (b) The neck of the flask is bent and the solution boiled. (c) After 3 weeks there is no evidence of fungal growth in the flask.

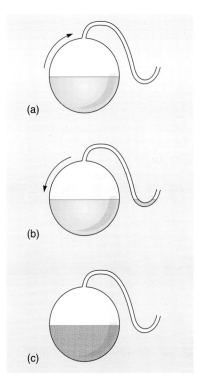

Figure 2.5 (a) The flask is tipped so that solution runs down into the 'U' (b) and then back to the body of the flask. (c) After 3 weeks the mixture is clouded with fungi.

Pasteur proved two things with his experiments: first, that boiling a liquid would kill any life that might be in it; second, that life would grow on suitable surfaces or in suitable solutions only if living particles arrived from elsewhere, i.e. that spontaneous generation did not occur. His findings helped establish that all life on Earth today comes from already living organisms; this fact is captured in the phrase 'the life cycle'. To explain what we mean by the life cycle, and how it fits in with Pasteur's findings, we must first discuss two of the three attributes of life: reproduction and growth. Before doing this though, we suggest that you carry out the first stages of an experiment to detect the presence of airborne fungi.

Activity 2.1   Investigating fungal particles in the air

In this activity you will carry out your own investigation into the fungal particles in the air around you. ◀

2.2   Reproduction and growth: the life cycle

Reproduction is the process by which organisms produce offspring. This simple statement belies a hugely complex sequence of events which usually begins with one organism finding a mate and ends with the birth of at least one new organism. Needless to say, there is tremendous variation in exactly how different kinds of organism produce their offspring. Some of this variation is discussed in later sections, but here we are concerned with things that organisms have in common. Two aspects of reproduction are universal. The first is that the offspring produced are initially small compared to their parents (Figure 2.6).

Figure 2.6   Size difference between adult and offspring: a strawberry frog (*Dendrobates pumilio*) carrying two of its tadpoles.

The offspring, therefore, have to grow. The period of **growth** varies between organisms, from minutes (for some bacteria) to centuries (for some trees). The size to which different organisms grow also varies. However, *all* offspring, and hence *all* organisms, have to grow.

The second universal aspect of reproduction is that only mature organisms are able to reproduce. Generally speaking, if an organism grows for long enough, it will be able to reproduce.

Putting these two aspects together: reproduction is followed by the growth of the offspring, which then reproduce to produce offspring themselves, which then grow … and so on. The repetition of reproduction followed by growth followed by reproduction is called the **life cycle**, and it is usually depicted as a circle (Figure 2.7).

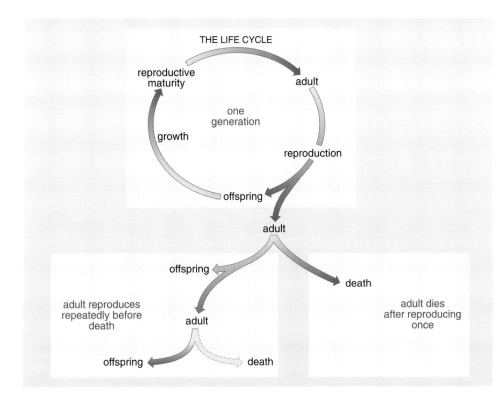

Figure 2.7 A generalized life cycle.

The circle represents the passage of time. Starting with 'offspring' and moving in a clockwise direction, the offspring grow and mature to become adult and then they themselves reproduce. One turn round the cycle represents the period of time from the birth of offspring to those offspring producing offspring of their own. In the generalized life cycle illustrated here, and in most depictions of life cycles, the adult drops out of the cycle between 'reproduction' and 'offspring'. In fact, the adults may go on to reproduce again, possibly several times until prevented from doing so by death or old age. The point is that one turn around the cycle covers the phases of life of that type of organism that are necessary to produce the next generation. The **generation time** is the time it takes a particular type of organism to go once around its life cycle. You will learn more about life cycles, and the extent to which they differ in detail between organisms of different types, later in this block. For now, you need to remember only that life cycles are universal to organisms and that one cycle is equivalent to one generation.

Question 2.1 Approximately how many years difference (if any) are there between the duration of the life cycle, the generation time and length of life for humans? ◄

The unusual feature of the fungal life cycle that fooled Pouchet is that fungal particles retain indefinitely their ability to grow. The particles are spores, special structures produced by fungi, which serve a similar function to seeds in plants. The spores could sit in Pasteur's 'U' bend for hundreds of years without losing their ability to grow.

● Under what conditions did Pasteur's experiments show that fungal spores lose their ability to grow?

○ When they are subjected to the heat of boiling water. (In fact, the spores of a few types of fungi will survive even boiling water!)

When the spores are in *favourable conditions* they will begin to grow. The concept of favourable conditions is an extremely important one in biology. Different organisms require different conditions of humidity, temperature and so on, in order to grow. What makes one type of organism different from another is the conditions in which it grows; each type of organism has a specific set of conditions in which it grows best. Thus, one type of fungus grows best on bread, another on rotten fruit and yet another on damp wallpaper.

○ Several different materials on which fungi grow have been mentioned. What do these materials have in common?

○ They are made of, or incorporate, once-living material.

Fungi of one sort or another will grow on almost anything that was once living, collectively called organic matter. Yet other fungi are able to grow on organic matter that is still living; one such is the common fungus (*Taenia pedis*) that causes cracks in the skin between the toes and itching, the condition known as athlete's foot.

The organic matter is the source of both material and energy for the fungus. Material is needed for the production and growth of new body parts, for repairing damage and for making new organisms (i.e. offspring). Energy is required for growth and for other processes that are essential for life. Material and energy are therefore essential requirements for maintaining life, for growth and for reproduction in all organisms. For example, as a tadpole changes from a pond-living, swimming organism to a land-based hopping frog it requires material from which to make new legs, new skin and new eyes. As a land-based frog, it continues to grow. Energy is required, not just to enable the tadpole to swim or the frog to hop, but also in the construction of new bone and skin from raw material.

So far, the discussion of the life processes of growth and reproduction has focused on whole organisms of different types (e.g. fungi, frogs). The whole organism is relatively easy to relate to, because that is what we usually see. We will next turn briefly to the level of molecules which make up organisms, a level that provides a somewhat different perspective on life processes.

2.3 Metabolism

All organisms (like everything else) are composed of combinations of chemical substances, i.e. molecules (Block 2, Section 6.3). Water is the major constituent of all organisms (Block 1). The bulk of the rest of the material of which an organism is made contains carbon. So water and carbon-based substances constitute an organism's biggest requirements. The way in which organisms obtain their carbon-based materials separate them into two groups: the autotrophs and the heterotrophs.

Autotrophs (from the Greek *auto* meaning 'self' and *troph* meaning 'feed') make their own carbon-based material starting with carbon dioxide. You have met the chemical reaction for this process in Block 2 (Section 7) and Block 3 (Section 18):

carbon dioxide + water → organic carbon + oxygen   (2.1)

○ What is missing from this chemical reaction?

○ The reaction requires the input of energy.

● Where does the energy come from and what is this process called?

○ The energy comes from the Sun and the process is called photosynthesis.

Photosynthesis is part of the carbon cycle. Solar energy is captured in very small structures called *chloroplasts*, in the leaves of plants. Carbon dioxide effectively reacts with water to produce simple, carbon-based, organic molecules, i.e. sugars. Nearly all living organisms depend either directly or indirectly on photosynthesis for their supply of organic molecules. (There are a few bacteria, called chemo-autotrophs, that produce sugars using different reactions that do not require solar energy.) Sugars serve two important roles. First, other organic molecules can be made from them. Second, they serve as a store for some of the Sun's energy. However, before we consider how the energy is released from storage, we need to look briefly at heterotrophs.

Heterotrophs (from the Greek *hetero* meaning 'other' and *troph* meaning 'feed') cannot make sugars by photosynthesis, so they rely on other organisms for their carbon-based materials. Essentially, heterotrophs either eat plants (if they are herbivores), eat other animals that have eaten plants (if they are carnivores) (Figure 2.8) or eat both plants and animals (if they are omnivores).

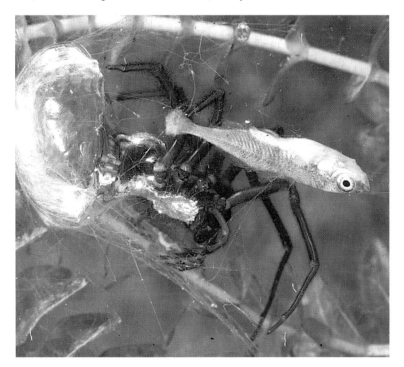

Figure 2.8 A carnivorous heterotroph (the water spider, *Argyroneta aquatica*) with a source of carbon-based materials (a stickleback, *Gasterosteus aculeatus*).

All animals are heterotrophs, which means that all the animals you see around you are ultimately dependent on plants for their carbon-based materials.

● Are the fungi we discussed earlier heterotrophs or autotrophs?

○ Fungi are heterotrophs because they rely on other organisms (e.g. leaves of the tea plant, fruit, human skin) for their carbon-based materials.

However an organism obtains its organic molecules, whether by photosynthesis or by eating them, these molecules undergo a series of chemical transformations which result in the production of the hundreds of different substances needed for life. The sum total of all these transformations is the organism's **metabolism**. Each type of organism has its own particular metabolism suited to its carbon source(s) and the substances it needs to make for body maintenance, repair and new growth. Maintenance involves the destruction of old material and its replacement with new. For example, in the average adult human up to 2.5 million red blood cells are destroyed every second and normally replaced at the same rate (so that the red blood cells you have in you now will have been entirely replaced in four months time). Skin, muscle, and internal organs are all also subject to a continuous programme of replacement for which metabolism is responsible. In addition, organisms get injured and damaged; making new bark (in the case of trees) or new skin (in the case of humans) to repair such damage also involves metabolism.

● Heterotrophs obtain their carbon-based materials ultimately from plants. From where do they obtain their energy?

○ From the same source: the carbon-based materials also supply energy.

We can now return to the process by which energy stored in organic molecules is released. The specific process is respiration and it is effectively the reverse of photosynthesis. Note that respiration at this level, the molecular level, is not the same as breathing. It is unfortunate, but quite common in biology, that one word has two different meanings. The process of **respiration** releases the energy stored in organic molecules in a series of highly controlled, very small steps. The end result is the production of carbon dioxide and water, so this process is an important part of the carbon cycle, as you saw in Section 8 of Block 2. The chemical reaction for respiration is:

$$\text{organic carbon} + \text{oxygen} \rightarrow \text{carbon dioxide} + \text{water} \qquad (2.2)$$

● What is missing from this chemical reaction?

○ The energy that is released.

● Is respiration part of metabolism?

○ Respiration involves the conversion of organic molecules into carbon dioxide and water. Thus, it is a chemical transformation occurring inside an organism and so it is part of metabolism.

The energy released by respiration is used to drive other parts of metabolism, to enable other chemical transformations to take place, and to enable animals to move. Moreover, respiration is just as important to autotrophs as it is to heterotrophs.

Question 2.2 Why do autotrophs need respiration, rather than simply using the Sun's energy directly to 'drive' metabolism? ◀

Organisms live over a period of time — centuries in the case of some trees. During its lifetime an organism will exhibit each of the attributes of life. However, at any particular moment an organism might not be growing (e.g. as an adult) or it might not be reproducing (e.g. as a juvenile). The one attribute of life that nearly all organisms reveal nearly all of the time is metabolism, although it is difficult to detect in seeds and even more so in fungal spores. In fact, only one organism has ever been found which appears to be able to survive a period of time without metabolizing at all, the brine shrimp (*Artemia franciscana*) (Figure 2.9). The idea that organisms are doing different things at different stages of their life cycles is picked up again in Section 6. Meanwhile, in Section 3, we introduce the cell, the building block of *all* living organisms.

Figure 2.9 The brine shrimp (*Artemia franciscana*), an organism which produces spore-like cysts which seem to be able to survive for some considerable time without metabolism (magnification ×5).

Activity 2.2 *Producing a glossary of biological terms*

A characteristic of biology that many students find difficult to get to grips with is its use of a large number of scientific terms. In this ongoing activity you will construct a personal glossary of important terms to help you cope with this aspect of the subject. ◄

Question 2.3 An adult male mayfly neither grows nor feeds, but flies around searching for a female with which to mate.

(a) Does the adult mayfly metabolize?

(b) All organisms have to grow, so how can the adult mayfly *not* grow?

(c) Is the adult mayfly an autotroph or an heterotroph?

(d) Apart from the adult mayfly, can you give an example of an organism that is neither growing nor photosynthesizing? ◄

Question 2.4 You wish to grow some mould on a piece of bread. You seal the bread in a clear plastic bag to stop it drying out. Do you think it makes any difference if you put the bread in a dark cupboard or leave it on a table in the light? Explain your answer. ◄

Question 2.5 Match each of statements (a)–(d) below to *one* of the following terms: (1) autotrophs, (2) heterotrophs, (3) metabolism, (4) respiration, (5) photosynthesis, (6) spontaneous generation, (7) reproduction, (8) life cycle.

(a) All the stages through which an organism passes until reproduction.

(b) The manufacture of sugars from carbon dioxide and water.

(c) The chemical transformations characteristic of living organisms.

(d) The release of energy from organic molecules. ◄

Question 2.6 Which of the terms (3)–(8) in Question 2.5 apply to autotrophs and which to heterotrophs? ◄

Question 2.7 It was stated earlier that metabolism 'is difficult to detect in seeds and even more so in fungal spores'. What might scientists measure to show that metabolism was taking place in fungal spores? ◄

2.4 Summary of Section 2

All living organisms have three attributes in common. *Reproduction* is the process by which an organism produces offspring. All organisms *grow*, both to increase in size and to repair damage. All organisms obtain the materials and energy they need through the chemical transformations of *metabolism*.

Autotrophs make their own organic molecules, the vast majority using photosynthesis. Heterotrophs obtain organic molecules from other organisms. Originally this material was produced by autotrophs.

All organisms release energy from organic molecules by the process of respiration.

The life cycle depicts all the stages an organism must go through from birth to parenthood, the duration of which is the generation time. During the life cycle, organisms are either growing and becoming mature, or they are mature and seeking to reproduce. Many organisms live for longer than one generation.

The three attributes of life are not necessarily evident at all stages of an organism's life.

3 The cell: unity within diversity

Cells are the smallest units of living things that show the three attributes of life: reproduction, growth and metabolism. Virtually all organisms are composed of cells; they are the basic unit of life.

The cell is an elegant and universal solution to a particular problem. The problem is that metabolism requires the intimate association between many different molecules; yet molecules have a tendency to drift about and become separated. Hence, the right molecules may be too far apart to interact with each other when needed. Metabolism — and thus life — would stop and start, depending on the proximity of particular molecules. The solution used by all organisms is to constrain the molecules needed for metabolism in small 'bags' by sheet-like structures called membranes. Thus constrained, the molecules remain relatively close together. The small amount of living material in each 'bag', including its enclosing membrane, is called the **cell**.

3.1 A typical cell

The cell has many components, but only three are considered in this block: the outer or cell membrane, the cytoplasm and the nucleus (Figures 3.1 and 3.2).

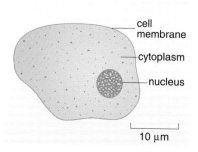

cell membrane

cytoplasm

nucleus

10 µm

Figure 3.1   A generalized eukaryotic cell showing the cell membrane, the cytoplasm and the nucleus. The term 'eukaryotic' means 'with a nucleus' and is explained later in this section. Note the scale bar from which you can deduce the actual size of the cell.

Figure 3.2   (a) Drawing of the top three layers of cells in a leaf of privet (*Ligustrum vulgare*). Note the dense packing of cells in the top two layers and the air spaces between the cells in the layer below. A nucleus can be seen in each of the cells. (b) Leaf of privet, torn to reveal the source of cells in (a).

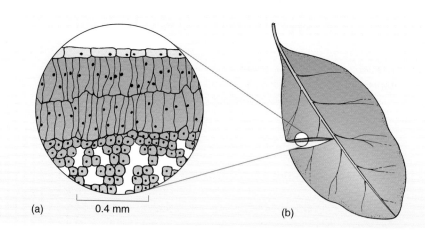

(a)   0.4 mm   (b)

The **cell membrane** is an extremely thin, yet very complex, structure. Its main function, as we have seen, is to constrain the molecules involved in metabolism. The membrane does this by restricting the movement of molecules from the inside of the cell to the outside, and vice versa. The latter restriction serves to protect the contents of the cell from harmful or unnecessary molecules.

⬤ Think of a large autotroph (e.g. a rose bush) composed of somewhere between 10^{10} and 10^{14} cells. What would be the problem if the cell membrane prevented the movement of *any* molecule into or out of any of the cells?

○ The problem would be that cells would not be able to get the things they need for metabolism and get rid of waste products; for example, water, oxygen and carbon dioxide would not be able to get into and out of the cells.

Recall that autotrophs use the Sun's energy to make sugars (simple organic molecules). Photosynthesis occurs in the chloroplasts found inside the thousands of cells of the leaf. But other parts of the plant (e.g. the roots), composed of thousands of cells which do not photosynthesize, also need sugar for metabolism. Sugar therefore has to be moved from the cells in the leaf where it is made to the cells of the root where it is needed. Thus, sugar has to leave the cell in which it is manufactured, by crossing the cell membrane, and it has to cross the cell membrane of the cell at its destination in order to participate in metabolism there.

Clearly, then, although most substances cannot cross the cell membrane, it is not a total barrier to the movement of substances. Rather than being *completely permeable* (which means allowing any substance to pass through), the cell membrane is **selectively permeable**, which means that it exerts some control over which substances can pass through it. Molecules of some substances (e.g. oxygen, carbon dioxide, water) move freely from one side of the cell membrane to the other by *diffusion*, which is simply the process by which molecules tend to move from areas where they are plentiful to areas where they are scarce. Sugars do not diffuse across the cell membrane. Instead, cells have special molecules in their membranes that assist in the process of moving sugar into and out of the cell.

The second component of the cell, the **cytoplasm** (pronounced 'sigh-toe-plaz-um'), is simply everything that is enclosed by the cell membrane other than the third component, the nucleus. Since most metabolism takes place in the cytoplasm, it contains the molecules which participate in this process. It also contains molecules which give the cell its shape, molecules which assist in the movement of other molecules and quite a lot of water. It also includes some very small structures, such as the chloroplasts in plants (where photosynthesis occurs).

The third component of the cell which we are considering in this block is the **nucleus** (plural: nuclei) (Figure 3.1), which is surrounded by a nuclear membrane. The nucleus contains the cell's genetic material, which stores all the information necessary for reproduction, growth and metabolism and which is copied from parent to offspring during reproduction. As you may know, the genetic material is the molecule DNA (standing for <u>d</u>eoxyribo<u>n</u>ucleic <u>a</u>cid). You will learn a lot more about DNA in Block 9.

Organisms in which the DNA is normally separated from the cytoplasm within nuclei, as just described, are known as **eukaryotes** (pronounced 'you-carry-oats'; their cells are known as *eukaryotic* cells). Not all organisms have nuclei, however. Organisms that do not have nuclei, and whose DNA is therefore free within the cytoplasm, are known as **prokaryotes** (and their cells described as *prokaryotic*). Most prokaryotes consist of single cells and are better known as *bacteria*. While some eukaryotes also consist of single cells, others consist of many cells.

○ How many membranes separate the DNA of a eukaryote from the cell's surroundings?

○ There are two membranes, the nuclear membrane separating the DNA from the cytoplasm and the cell membrane which encloses all the cell's contents including the nucleus.

Question 3.1 (a) Name a type of molecule that requires assistance to move across the cell membrane.

(b) How do molecules that do not require assistance (e.g. oxygen) move across the cell membrane? ◄

Question 3.2 Which one of the following statements is wrong?

(a) The nucleus contains DNA.

(b) The nucleus is surrounded by cytoplasm.

(c) A eukaryotic cell contains a nucleus.

(d) A prokaryotic cell contains no genetic material. ◄

3.2 The eukaryotic cell cycle

Many organisms are composed of huge numbers of cells — they are **multicellular organisms**. It is difficult to give an exact figure for the number of cells because there are usually too many to count. As a guide, though, it has been estimated that your brain alone contains somewhere in the region of 10^{10} cells. The cells in a multicellular organism all arise by cell division from a single cell, called the *zygote*. We define zygote in Section 6, when we consider sexual and asexual reproduction, but 'the first cell of an organism' is a close approximation to a definition and will suffice for now. All the cells of a multicellular organism are descendants of the zygote and normally they all contain exactly the same genetic material. To explain how this comes about, we need to consider the cell cycle.

The principles of the **cell cycle** are the same for all organisms, although there are subtle differences between prokaryotes and eukaryotes. For simplicity, here we will consider only the eukaryotic cell cycle (Figure 3.3). The zygote grows until it is sufficiently large to undergo cell division, during which it divides to produce two **progeny cells**. The zygote itself effectively disappears, leaving only the two progeny cells. The two progeny cells now grow until they too are sufficiently large to divide, and then they each produce two progeny cells. The sequence progeny cell–growth–cell division (boxed in Figure 3.3) repeats again and again. It can be depicted in a similar way to the life cycle (Figure 3.4).

Figure 3.3 A sequence of cell divisions. Each cell produces two progeny cells when it divides. The letter A represents the start, and the letter B the finish, of one cell cycle.

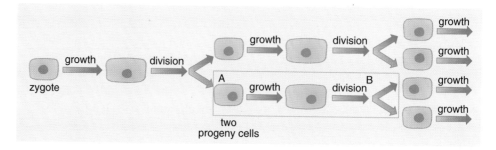

The cell cycle can take anything from a few hours to many weeks to complete. The rate at which a cell proceeds through the cycle depends on many factors, including the type of organism, the type of cell and its size, and the environment in which the cell is growing. There is also variation in the duration of cell division itself. For instance, cells in the roots of many plants take about 12 hours to divide, those in the gut of a mouse take about 17 hours and those in human skin take about 24 hours.

It is important to appreciate that the cell cycle is continuous. Nevertheless, for convenience of explanation, it can be divided into four phases (Figure 3.5). The longest phase, and the one with the most variable duration, is when most of the cell's increase in size takes place. This phase, which is referred to as **growth I**, can be speeded up or slowed down quite considerably, depending upon the prevailing conditions, and so it has the greatest influence on how long the cell cycle takes to complete. In dormant organisms (e.g. plant seeds), cells are usually held in this phase until conditions are suitable for them to grow. After growth I, the DNA molecules within the cell's nucleus are copied, during the **replication** phase, to produce two identical sets of DNA molecules. A second, shorter, growth phase, **growth II**, follows. These three phases, growth I, replication and growth II, are collectively referred to as **interphase**. The cycle finishes with **cell division** which comprises two short, but crucial, episodes. In the first, called mitosis (which we will consider in detail in Section 3.3), one copy of each DNA molecule is distributed to each end of the parent cell. In the second, the parent cell makes a new membrane across its middle and, in so doing, divides to create two progeny cells, each with a set of genetic material identical to that of the parent cell.

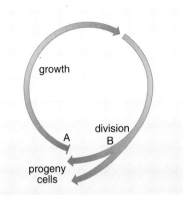

Figure 3.4 The cell cycle in outline. The letters A and B correspond to the same points in the cycle shown in Figure 3.3.

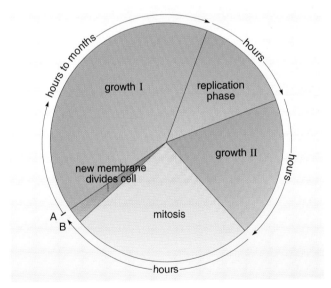

Figure 3.5 The eukaryotic cell cycle in detail. The duration given for each of the four phases is very approximate and varies according to the conditions in which the cell finds itself. Collectively the area shaded green is known as interphase. The letters A and B correspond to the same points in the cycle shown in Figures 3.3 and 3.4.

Within the nucleus, DNA molecules are attached to other molecules (mainly proteins) to form structures known as **chromosomes**. During interphase most DNA exists as very long, thin threads; this makes it very difficult to see chromosomes even through a microscope. During mitosis, however, the DNA becomes tightly coiled, which makes the chromosomes very much more conspicuous (Figure 3.6).

Figure 3.6 Chromosomes are conspicuous during mitosis, particularly when special dyes are used to make them stand out from the background. This photograph shows chromosomes in a cell of the broad bean, *Vicia faba* (magnification ×2 000).

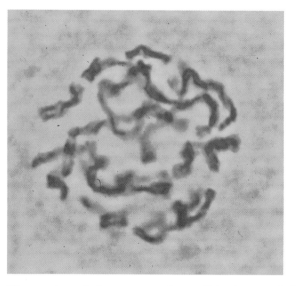

The number of chromosomes in a cell is characteristic of each type of organism. For example, a human cell has a set of 46 chromosomes, some of which are long and some of which are short. In any other cell from the same human (or another human of the same sex; see below) there would also be a set of 46 chromosomes identical in size and shape to the first set. In humans, 44 chromosomes are matching twins, i.e. there are 22 pairs of chromosomes. These matching chromosomes are called **autosomes**. Eukaryotes, such as humans, in which the autosomes normally exist as pairs, are referred to as being **diploid**. The remaining two chromosomes, known as the **sex chromosomes** because they determine whether someone is male or female, do not always have a matching twin. Females do have a matching pair of X chromosomes, but males have one X and one Y chromosome which do not match.

Question 3.3 (a) During growth phase I are there (i) more, (ii) fewer, (iii) about the same number or (iv) exactly the same number of chromosomes as molecules of DNA in the nucleus?

(b) Is a DNA molecule (i) shorter, (ii) longer, (iii) about the same length or (iv) exactly the same length during mitosis as it is during interphase? ◀

Activity 3.1 Analysing and improving a description of the cell cycle

A good way to improve your own writing skills is to critically analyse someone else's writing, for both accuracy and clarity, and then to improve upon it. In this activity, you will do this with a description of the cell cycle. ◀

3.3 Mitosis

Each progeny cell must have a complete set of the parent cell's chromosomes so that each has a copy of all the organism's genetic information. The process by which this is achieved is known as **mitosis** (pronounced 'my-toe-sis'). For simplicity, mitosis is described here for a diploid cell with just four chromosomes (i.e. two pairs of matching chromosomes). However, the same principles would apply if there were 18, 46 or any other number of chromosomes in the cell.

Mitosis begins when the DNA molecules in the nucleus become tightly coiled, so making the chromosomes visible using a microscope. As each DNA molecule made a copy of itself during the replication phase of interphase (Figure 3.5), the four chromosomes consist of eight rather than four DNA molecules at this stage. Somewhere along its length, each DNA molecule is joined to its copy. This point of attachment is called the **centromere**, and its position is characteristic of each chromosome. In this state of attachment, each DNA molecule of a pair (plus its associated protein molecules) is called a **chromatid** (Figure 3.7).

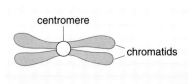

Figure 3.7   Drawing of a chromosome to show the two chromatids joined at the centromere.

○ For any particular autosomal chromatid, how many of the other chromatids in the same cell have exactly the same size and shape? (Look at Figure 3.8a.)

○ Three, the one that is attached to it and the two that make up the chromosome's twin chromosome.

○ The common fruit-fly (*Drosophila melanogaster*), which is seen hovering around fruit in the summer months, has eight chromosomes. How many chromatids are there in one of its cells at the start of mitosis?

○ At the start of mitosis, a fruit-fly cell has 16 chromatids.

Once started, mitosis is a continuous process. During the earliest phase of mitosis (known as **prophase**), the membrane which usually surrounds the chromosomes disappears, so that the cell no longer has a nucleus. The loss of the nuclear membrane is necessary to allow unrestrained movement of the four chromosomes within the cell, each chromosome now consisting of a pair of identical chromatids joined together at the centromere (Figure 3.8a).

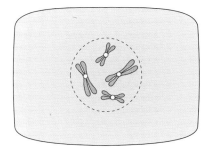

(a) prophase

Delicate threads anchored at one or other end of the cell become attached to the centromeres. During the next phase (known as **metaphase**) these threads exert tension on the chromosomes, eventually aligning them across the middle of the cell (Figure 3.8b).

The chromatids then separate, so that each becomes a chromosome in its own right. One member of each former pair of chromatids is drawn to one end of the cell, while its partner is drawn to the other end. This phase of mitosis is known as **anaphase** (Figure 3.8c).

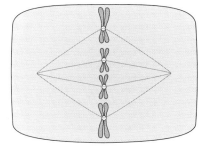

(b) metaphase

Once the chromosomes reach one or other end of the cell, the threads which were attached to them disappear. There is now a set of four chromosomes clustered at one end of the cell and an equivalent set of four chromosomes clustered at the other end (Figure 3.8d), a phase of mitosis known as **telophase**.

The DNA molecules then start to become uncoiled. At the same time, a nuclear membrane forms around each chromosome cluster so that the cell temporarily contains two nuclei. Mitosis has now finished, but to complete the cell cycle, the cell itself must divide in two.

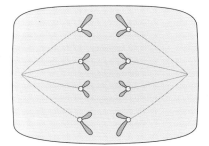

(c) anaphase

The division of the cytoplasm between the two new progeny cells is achieved by the production of a new membrane exactly where the chromosomes aligned across the middle of the cell during metaphase. (The start of this process is visible in Figure 3.8d.) Once the new membrane divides the cell, cell division is complete; one cell has become two. These two cells are now in interphase.

Figure 3.8   The phases of mitosis. (a) Prophase: the four chromosomes each consist of two chromatids attached at a centromere. (b) Metaphase: the four chromosomes are aligned across the centre of the cell with threads attached to their centromeres. (c) Anaphase: the pairs of chromatids separate in each of the four chromosomes, giving rise to eight separate chromosomes which are drawn to opposite ends of the cell. (d) Telophase: four chromosomes arrive at each end of the cell.

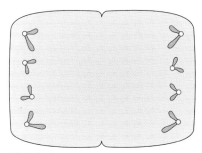

(d) telophase

Each of the two new cells contains an identical copy of the genetic material. However, each of the two new cells is half the size of the original cell just before mitosis began. A period of growth, during which the cells increase in size (i.e. the 'growth I' and 'growth II' phases of the cell cycle) and the DNA molecules replicate, is therefore required before the new cells can themselves undergo mitosis and cell division.

Activity 3.2 _Drawing a diagram of mitosis_

This activity will help to consolidate your understanding of mitosis by producing a diagram showing the successive stages. ◀

Question 3.4 How many chromosomes would you expect to see in a human cell during anaphase? ◀

Question 3.5 Explain why each of the following statements is wrong:

(a) There are always two chromosomes in every diploid cell.

(b) There are always two chromatids in every chromosome.

(c) Each chromosome has its own nucleus.

(d) Mitosis is part of interphase.

(e) A cell with no nucleus must be prokaryotic. ◀

3.4 Variations on a theme

Figure 3.9 (a) Four different sorts of cell from the human body (not to scale). (b) Diagram to show the relative sizes of four different cells.

It is obvious from Figure 3.2a that the cells of a leaf are not all the same; they have different sizes and are different shapes. Most multicellular organisms contain lots of different sorts of cells. Figure 3.9a illustrates four of the few hundred different types of cell from the human body and Figure 3.9b shows the relative sizes of three human cells and a bacterial cell.

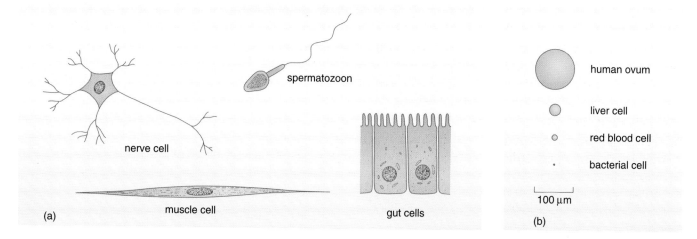

The different types of cell carry out different tasks. The cells on the surface of the leaf help protect it; they contain no chloroplasts. Those inside the leaf do contain chloroplasts and so carry out photosynthesis. Your skin cells provide protection from the external environment, your nerve cells help you to sense your surroundings and your muscle cells enable you to move. The cells of multicellular organisms each do a few things very well; they are said to be _specialized_. When they become specialized, some types of cell lose the ability to divide. Red blood cells are very good at carrying oxygen around the body, but they cannot divide. Since red blood cells are continually being destroyed in large numbers, other cells have to do the dividing for them in order to replace the lost cells. The cells which specialize in dividing to produce red blood cells are found in the bone marrow.

All this specialization raises the question 'how is it achieved?' After all, the cells in a multicellular organism are all derived ultimately from the zygote. Mitotic cell division ensures that each cell contains exactly the same genetic information as that present in the zygote. But some of this information is about how to make skin cells, some of it is about how to make nerve cells, some of it is about how to make muscle cells, and so on. If a cell were to 'obey' all the instructions present in its DNA it could not become specialized. Therefore, only some of the genetic information present in every one of an organism's cells is 'switched on' in any particular cell at any particular time.

Activity 2.2 (continued)   *Your glossary of biological terms*

You may have been adding to your glossary as you read this section, but if not, look back through Section 3 and add new terms as appropriate to your glossary. There are almost 30 bold terms in this section, so building your glossary will be particularly important to aid your memory. ◀

3.5   Summary of Section 3

The cell is the smallest living unit capable of reproduction, growth and metabolism.

At one time or another, all organisms exist as a single cell, the zygote. Some organisms remain as single cells throughout their lives. On the other hand, multicellular organisms are single-celled only as zygotes.

The cell is surrounded by a cell membrane, which constrains the cytoplasm and is selectively permeable. Each cell contains DNA. The DNA is enclosed in a nuclear membrane in eukaryotic cells, but not in prokaryotic cells.

Chromosomes comprise DNA molecules associated with other molecules. During mitosis the DNA is fully coiled, enabling chromosomes to be seen under the microscope (particularly when special dyes are used). There are two types of chromosomes: autosomes are paired in diploid eukaryotic cells; sex chromosomes, which are designated X and Y in humans, may or may not be paired.

There are four phases to the cell cycle: growth I, replication, growth II and mitosis. DNA molecules are copied during the replication phase of the cell cycle and then shared equally between the two progeny cells during mitosis, so that each contains a complete copy of the DNA present in the original cell. Mitosis is a continuous process but four phases — prophase, metaphase, anaphase and telophase — can be recognized.

The cells in multicellular organisms are specialized to perform different functions. Specialization results from each cell 'obeying' only some of the instructions contained in its DNA.

4 Diversity: the spice of life

You saw in Section 2 that all living organisms share three fundamental attributes: the processes of reproduction, growth and metabolism. You then saw, in Section 3, that all living organisms are also united in their construction since they are composed of one or more of the basic units known as cells. While most multicellular organisms are composed of huge numbers of individual cells, altogether there are only a few hundred different types of cell (Section 3.4).

In contrast to this impressive display of *unity*, this section is concerned with *diversity*. Specifically, it is concerned with the manifestation of life in an enormous number (i.e. tens of millions) of different types of organism, or species. Among the skills emphasized in this section are therefore those which relate to classification, since it is important to be able to 'see the wood for the trees' among this great variety of species.

4.1 Species

You are probably familiar with the expression 'the human species'. But what does the word 'species' mean? It must mean that members of our species (*Homo sapiens*) possess one or more characters in common that make it sensible (a) to group or classify humans together and (b) to distinguish humans from other species. In the present context, the term **character** is used to mean a characteristic or trait. All other species must likewise have some distinguishing character(s).

○ From general knowledge, what two characters are generally implied about organisms that are said to belong to the same species?

○ Most obviously, members of the same species tend to be quite similar to one another in appearance, behaviour, etc. Perhaps less obviously, members of the same species are capable of producing offspring that clearly belong to the same species — and *only* the same species — as themselves.

While we all know roughly what we mean when we say that a particular organism belongs to one species rather than another, in practice it is remarkably difficult to give a precise definition of the word 'species'. This is not dissimilar to the situation we encountered when we tried to pin down the precise meaning of the word 'life' in Section 2. (Incidentally, the word 'species' is both singular and plural: one species, several species.)

Of the two characters of **species** suggested above, many biologists prefer to give priority to the ability of organisms of a particular species to produce offspring, all of which are members of the same species as themselves. Such biologists emphasize the **reproductive isolation** of species from one another. Two adult humans of the opposite sex are usually capable of mating and producing more humans (their offspring). This is true also of pairs belonging to other familiar species, such as the common chimpanzee (*Pan troglodytes*), the domestic horse (*Equus caballus*), the donkey (*Equus asinus*), the lion (*Panthera leo*), the tiger (*Panthera tigris*), etc. However, as members of different species, a human and a common chimpanzee are not capable of producing offspring together.

Consider what happens when mating takes place between a horse and a donkey. The offspring of a female horse mated to a male donkey is a mule, while that of a female donkey mated to a male horse is a hinny. Does this mean that horses and donkeys are not truly separate species after all? In fact, mules are infertile (i.e. they are incapable of producing offspring themselves) and hinnies have considerably reduced fertility. Thus, although a horse mated to a donkey can produce offspring, those offspring represent reproductive 'dead ends'. Similarly, although lions and tigers are distinct species, they too have been known to produce (relatively infertile) offspring together, but only in captivity when separated from members of the opposite sex of their own species. In fact, a number of animal species are known to interbreed even in the wild. Some even produce what appear to be fully-fertile hybrids (in this context, the offspring of a mating between two distinct species is called a hybrid). Nevertheless, hybridization between species in the wild occurs only under rather limited circumstances, for instance where the geographical ranges of two similar species overlap only slightly. Because hybridization between species is considerably more common in plants than in animals, it is particularly difficult to define plant species in terms of reproductive isolation.

These various exceptions mean that biologists have to qualify the preferred basis for defining species. Organisms are said to belong to different species if adults of the opposite sex are never capable of producing *fully fertile* offspring under *natural conditions* or if hybridization is *extremely* rare for most of the population of that organism. Unfortunately, all sorts of 'operational' difficulties can complicate attempts to classify organisms into distinct species. For instance, if similar-looking animals live in different parts of the world, how could we establish with certainty whether or not they belong to the same species? We might move one or both of them to the same location. However, if they fail to interbreed there, is this because they belong to different species, or is it because the prevailing conditions are insufficiently natural for one or both of them? Moreover, we obviously cannot apply the 'fertility' test to establish whether or not a fossil and a living animal, or two fossil animals, belong to the same species, or to decide whether two plants that reproduce without sex (e.g. by producing bulbs) belong to the same species.

In practice, therefore, most organisms are classified into one species or another on the basis of their appearance and/or their behaviour (e.g. the songs of different bird species), rather than on whether or not they can interbreed. This allows us to classify fossil as well as living, and non-sexual as well as sexual, organisms into species. The trouble is that many perfectly 'valid' species (e.g. different groups of animals that are *known* not to breed together) look virtually identical even to experts, while sometimes members of the same species can look very different from one another. The latter is obviously true of dogs (as well as other domestic and agricultural animals), although the reason here is undoubtedly human interference. However, there are many wild species that are described as **polymorphic** because they exist in a number of highly distinctive 'types' with different appearance or *morphology* (Figure 4.1). There are also species in which the sexes are strikingly different from one another, a phenomenon known as **sexual dimorphism** (Figure 4.2). In each case, if one didn't know about the breeding behaviour of the animals concerned, one might well assume that they belonged to different species.

Figure 4.1 The two-spot ladybird (*Adalia bipunctata*) comes in both a 'typical' and a dark (or melanic) form.

(a)

(b)

Figure 4.2 (a) Male and female elephant seals (*Mirounga angustirostris*) differ greatly in size, while (b) male and female peafowl (*Pavo cristatus*) have strikingly different plumage.

4.2   Recognizing and labelling species

Biologists would like to be able to classify all living (and fossil) organisms into one or another species. Ideally this would be on the basis of their reproductive behaviour, but generally it is on the basis of their appearance and/or other aspects of their behaviour. Intrinsic to this procedure is, first, *recognizing* species as distinct entities and, second, giving these entities unique *labels*. It is important to realize that a labelled category (such as a species) ought not to have been created in the first place, and individual organisms cannot be placed consistently into one category rather than another, unless we can reliably identify *significant* differences between organisms that belong to different species.

You probably already know that the scientific label of our own species is *Homo sapiens*. You may also know that this Latin label is generally translated as 'thinking man' (with the immodest implication that we are better at thinking than other species and the inaccurate implication that males are somehow more significant than females). What you may not fully appreciate as you see and hear our scientific label bandied about is that it is *not* just a fancy alternative to the word 'human'. Rather, its use implies acceptance of all sorts of knowledge about how our species relates to other species, knowledge that may be commonplace to our generation, but which would have been (quite literally) *unthinkable* in earlier times.

Consider someone who decides to take up bird-watching as a hobby. He or she would not, of course, be starting from scratch. Several distinctive species (e.g. the robin), as well as some distinctive categories of birds (e.g. wildfowl, gulls), would already be familiar. However, the novice would soon be able to distinguish between far more species and also classify many more species into groups that are widely accepted as 'natural'. For instance, the person would learn to distinguish between blue tits, great tits and coal tits (see title page) and also realize that tits form a group (or family) of species distinct from other groups such as finches, warblers and sparrows (Figure 4.3). With perseverance, the bird-watcher will develop the knowledge and skills needed to distinguish (often instantly) between the 300 or so bird species regularly found in the British Isles, sometimes on the basis of extremely subtle differences in their plumage or calls.

(a)

(b)

(c)

Figure 4.3 Representative species of three bird families. (a) Goldfinch (*Carduelis carduelis*), (b) willow warbler (*Phylloscopus trochilus*) and (c) tree sparrow (*Passer montanus*).

Is it possible, however, that agreement about what constitutes a particular bird species, or which species form 'natural' groups (families), exists only because we uncritically accept the published opinions of 'experts'? An expedition to the Arfak Mountains of New Guinea in 1928 by the American biologist Ernst Mayr provided an opportunity to test this possibility. Before setting out, Mayr studied the relevant bird collections in European museums. When he arrived in New Guinea, he hired local hunters to collect specimens of all the different birds they knew of in the region. Mayr found that the Arfak hunters recognized 136 distinct types of bird. The match between these types and the species recognized by European biologists on the basis of museum specimens was almost perfect. In fact, the Arfak hunters lumped together just one pair of very similar species. The very high level of agreement between two such different cultures strongly suggests that our division of organisms into distinct species is a true reflection of the natural world.

Of course, birds are a rather conspicuous, well-studied group of species. Moreover, only about 9 000 species of bird have been described in total, of which about 500 have been seen in the British Isles at some time. Many other groups are far less familiar, and some of these are known to include *many* species (e.g. getting on for a million species of insect have been described). It is hardly surprising, therefore, that while all known bird species have a common name (in English and several other languages) which can easily be looked up, this is *not* true of the majority of species.

● Why does *every* known species not have a common name in (say) English?

○ Inevitably, many species will be much more familiar to people who live in countries where English is not the main language. These species may therefore have been given common names in other languages. However, it is hardly a practical proposition to give a million insect species, many of which are rather inconspicuous, different common names in *any* everyday language.

● What advantages are there in *every* fully-described species (i.e. even those that *do* have common names) having a unique label that is used by scientists throughout the world?

○ Referring to a species by a single label accepted throughout the world is *essential* for scientific communication. If biologists in different countries referred to a species only by its common name in their own language, biologists elsewhere would not know whether the species was the same as one they were studying.

Incidentally, the problem of a species having different common names can apply even within a single language and/or country. For instance, *Galium aparine*, a common British plant widely known as either 'cleavers' or 'goosegrass', has at least 20 other common names including 'sticky willy'.

Another advantage of species having unique scientific labels is that sometimes the same common name is used to describe different species in different parts of the world. You might think that the 'Christmas card' robin (*Erithacus rubecula*) is sufficiently familiar and distinctive to be referred to safely by its common name. However, when North Americans use the word 'robin' they usually mean *Turdus migratorius*, a much larger thrush that also happens to have a reddish breast.

4.3 Classifying species

So far we have concentrated on the division of organisms into species. We now turn our attention to the classification of species into larger groups (e.g. bird species into families).

An important reason for classifying species is to enable us to deal efficiently with the vast number of different species known to exist. While there may be a few people who can identify all 9 000 or so known bird species, there is surely no-one who can do this for the almost one million known species of insect. In order to systematically record all the information known about (say) insects, and efficiently retrieve that information when needed, insects have to be classified into a succession of categories between 'insects' (one group of a million species) at one end of the spectrum and individual species (a million single-species groups) at the other.

Classifying anything (whether birds, insects, volcanoes (Block 3, Section 8) or library books) depends on recognizing similarities between individuals to enable them to be grouped together, and differences to enable one group to be distinguished from another. There are, of course, many ways in which species *could* be classified. For instance, we could distinguish between species that (at least some) humans consider edible and those considered inedible. Alternatively, we could group together species generally regarded as pests, those known to be poisonous or sources of medicine, those that make good pets, and so on. The basis of such classifications is how useful (or otherwise) the species are to us but they don't tell us much about what the organisms are like. However, there is a much more fundamental basis for classifying species, which is that species do seem to cluster into 'natural' groups.

Activity 4.1 Devising a classification scheme for living things

This activity will help you to appreciate the important scientific process of classification, by asking you to identify similarities and differences in a collection of organisms and hence to classify them.◀

Most of us would be in agreement about certain 'natural' groupings of species. For example, birds are obviously distinct from mammals, fishes, insects, etc. All birds share a number of major characters (e.g. they all have feathers and beaks) which are distinct from the characters of any other group (mammals, fishes and insects do not have feathers and beaks). Among birds, more specific characters allow us to distinguish smaller groupings, such as waterfowl, birds of prey, songbirds, etc. Among songbirds, tits are distinct from finches, warblers, sparrows, etc. Certainly the broadest of these 'natural' groupings of species has been recognized since at least the time of the ancient Greeks, while a 'natural' classification had been worked out in considerable detail by early in the 19th century. Indeed, thousands of species were fitted into a 'natural' classification, still largely accepted by biologists today, before people knew *why* there were 'natural' links between species. The process now known to be responsible for species falling into such 'natural' groups is, of course, evolution.

During the course of evolution, a group of ancestral vertebrate animals (i.e. animals with backbones) gave rise to several distinct sub-groups of vertebrates (e.g. birds, mammals). Each of these gave rise to further sub-groups (e.g. ancestral birds evolved into waterfowl, birds of prey, songbirds, etc.), which gave rise to further sub-groups (e.g. ancestral songbirds evolved into tits, finches, sparrows, etc.), and so on until we reach the level of the individual modern species (e.g. the blue tit) (Figure 4.4). In their 'natural' classification of living (and, indeed, extinct) species, biologists aim to reflect this 'top down' splitting of groups of organisms into ever smaller groups and, in so doing, to trace the course of evolution. In an alternative depiction, Figure 4.5 shows the blue tit species 'nested' into successively larger groups of organisms (i.e. tit species, songbird species, bird species, vertebrate species).

Figure 4.4 Schematic diagram to show how a group of ancestral vertebrate animals gave rise successively to several distinct sub-groups of vertebrates during the course of evolution.

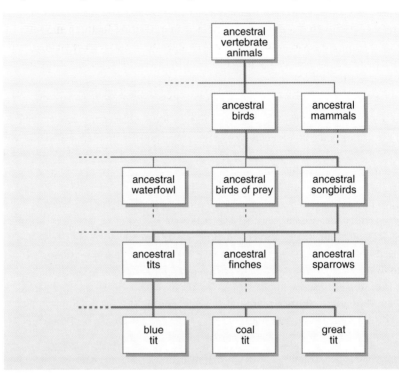

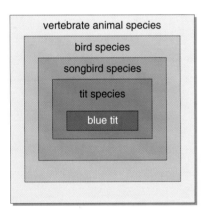

Figure 4.5 How the blue tit fits into successively larger groups of vertebrate animals.

○ All blue tits are very similar to one another, which is one of two main reasons why we recognize them as a particular species. What is the other main reason?

○ Blue tits breed with one another to produce more blue tits, but they do *not* breed with other species.

Blue tits also share lots of features with other species of tit. If they didn't, we wouldn't recognize the category 'tit'. However, a blue tit has fewer features in common with a coal tit or a great tit than it does with other blue tits. Similarly, tit species have fewer features in common with other songbird species than they do with one another, songbird species have fewer features in common with other types of bird species than they do with one another, and so on.

○ Why do the members of successively larger, and therefore more inclusive, groups necessarily have fewer and fewer features in common?

○ Because they are ever more distantly related to one another, their common ancestor having lived that much longer ago. {An appropriate analogy might be that first cousins (who share the same grandparents but have different parents) are likely to possess fewer characters in common than brothers and sisters (who share the same parents).}

Importantly, while the number of features shared decreases as we move up the classification hierarchy, the features that *are* shared become increasingly more fundamental to our recognition of what constitutes a 'bird'. We recognize a blue tit as a blue tit because it has a particular blue and yellow colouring, but we recognize it as a bird because of its more fundamental characteristics. If we were asked to classify a blue tit, an owl and a blue and yellow fish, we would have no hesitation in grouping the blue tit and the owl together on the basis of their shared fundamental characters of beaks and feathers (among other things).

Pioneer biologists were able to fit species into a 'natural' system of classification because they recognized patterns in the way species shared some features and not others. Only some time later was it realized that most of these patterns exist as a direct consequence of the evolutionary relationships between species. Each species had descended from a line of ancestral species, some of which gave rise to *many* descendent species which therefore tend to have features in common.

Having considered the basis of a 'natural' or evolutionary classification of species, we will now take a brief look at the classification scheme itself. At the very broadest level, organisms are grouped into three **domains**. Two of the domains — the **Archaea** (pronounced 'are-key-ah') and the **Bacteria** — include all the prokaryotes. The third domain, which includes all the eukaryotes, is known as the **Eukarya**. We will not distinguish between the prokaryotic domains in this block nor consider how they are subdivided (you will learn more about them in Block 12). However, the Eukarya is further subdivided into four **kingdoms**: the **Protoctista** (formerly, but less accurately, known as Protista), the **Fungi**, the **Plantae** and the **Animalia**. Within any particular domain or kingdom most species share just a few key features; otherwise they are rather diverse (i.e. most are only distantly related to one another). Much of the following information about domains and kingdoms is summarized in Table 4.1, to which you might like to refer as you read on.

Table 4.1 Summary of information about the classification of organisms into domains and kingdoms.

domain Archaea	domain Bacteria	domain Eukarya			
		kingdom Protoctista (protoctists)	kingdom Fungi (fungi)	kingdom Plantae (plants)	kingdom Animalia (animals)
prokaryotic		eukaryotic	eukaryotic	eukaryotic	eukaryotic
unicellular (mostly)		unicellular (mostly)	multicellular (mostly)	multicellular (mostly)	multicellular
some autotrophic, some heterotrophic		some autotrophic, some heterotrophic	heterotrophic	autotrophic (almost all)	heterotrophic

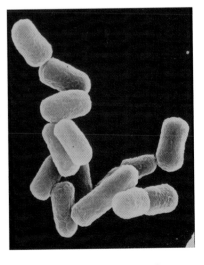

Figure 4.6 *Escherichia coli*, a rod-shaped bacterium commonly found in the gut. (Magnification ×14 000.) False colour has been added to the image to enhance the visibility of the bacterial cells.

All members of the domains Archaea and Bacteria are, by definition, prokaryotic and most of them are unicellular (Figure 4.6).

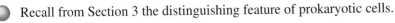

Recall from Section 3 the distinguishing feature of prokaryotic cells.

The cells' DNA is not enclosed in a nuclear membrane as it is in the case of eukaryotic cells.

Prokaryotes are perhaps the most widely dispersed of all organisms, some being capable of living in even the most extreme of environments, such as hot volcanic springs and in strong solutions of acid or salt (brine). Some are autotrophic and others heterotrophic. Although some cause serious diseases in humans, including tuberculosis, leprosy and typhoid, we are also dependent upon them because of the crucial part they play in the carbon cycle (Block 2) as well as the cycles of other elements. They were the first living organisms to arise on Earth, some 4 billion years ago, and they had it to themselves for about 2 billion years.

Members of the kingdom Protoctista (referred to informally as protoctists) are also mostly unicellular, although their cells are eukaryotic (Figure 4.7). Again, some are autotrophic and others heterotrophic. Protoctists are responsible for many diseases in humans, including amoebic dysentery and malaria. Protoctists come in such a wide variety of forms that classifying them together in a single 'kingdom' may say more about our lack of knowledge about them than about the evolutionary course they followed.

Figure 4.7 Examples of protoctists. (a) *Trypanosoma* (in human blood), which causes the disease 'sleeping sickness'. (Magnification ×3 000.) (b) A foraminiferan (*Operculina ammanoides*). (Magnification ×5.) The shells of these organisms are an important constituent of some carbonate rocks (Block 2, Section 8.5.3).

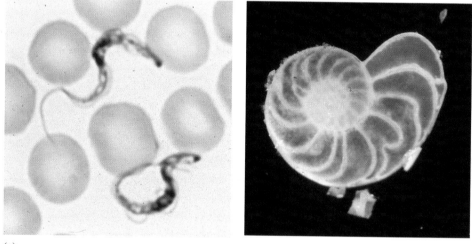

(a)   (b)

The final three kingdoms (which, of course, are referred to informally as fungi, plants and animals), include the vast majority of multicellular eukaryotic organisms. As such, they will be more familiar to you than the mostly unicellular organisms already discussed. While *almost* all multicellular organisms belong to one of these three kingdoms, *some* fungi and plants exist as both unicellular and multicellular types. Unfortunately, in biology there is usually an exception to every rule!

Question 4.1   Which two characters would allow you to distinguish fairly reliably between fungi, plants and animals? ◄

In order to show how organisms are classified within kingdoms, we will concentrate on the animal kingdom because it is the one with which you are likely to be most familiar. Similar principles apply in the case of other kingdoms, but generally speaking more detailed knowledge is required to appreciate the relevant distinctions. We will illustrate the classification scheme with two particularly familiar animals: the domestic cat (*Felis catus*) and the domestic dog (*Canis familiaris*). You may like to refer to Figure 4.8 as you read on.

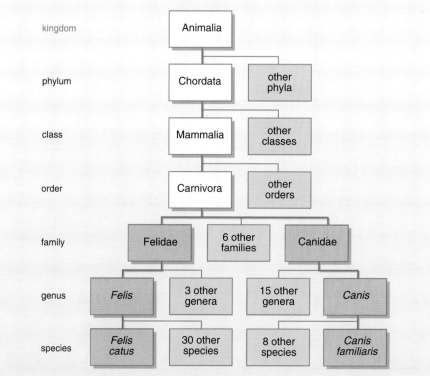

Figure 4.8 The scientific classification of the domestic cat (*Felis catus*) and domestic dog (*Canis familiaris*).

The **phylum** (plural: phyla) (pronounced 'file-um' and 'file-ah', respectively) is the broadest division within a kingdom. Different phyla represent fundamentally different body plans. Almost 100 living phyla are recognized across the three domains. The animal kingdom is divided into 20–30 living phyla by most experts. It is an unfortunate fact of life that experts do not agree on the number of different phyla. The problem stems primarily from whether one regards a particular body plan as 'fundamentally' different from other body plans or less than 'fundamentally' different. But it is exacerbated by the enormous range in the number of species encompassed by different phyla, however these are defined. With about one million living species, no biologist would hesitate to grant phylum status to the distinctive arthropods (i.e. animals with external skeletons and jointed legs, such as insects, spiders and lobsters). Other important animal phyla with many species are the molluscs (snails, etc.) and the chordates (mainly animals with backbones, such as ourselves). However, many biologists are reluctant to call even quite distinctive groups of animals separate phyla if they contain just a few species. A somewhat longer list of phyla appears in Box 5.1. As animals with backbones, domestic cats and dogs are classified together as members of the kingdom Animalia and of the phylum Chordata.

Each phylum is divided into a number of *classes*. Among the classes into which the chordates are subdivided are those into which fishes, amphibians, reptiles, birds and mammals are classified. Because they are warm-blooded, possess fur, give birth to live young and produce milk, domestic cats and dogs are still classified together within the class Mammalia.

Each class is divided into a number of *orders*. Cats and dogs remain classified together within the order Carnivora. Of course, the words 'carnivore' and 'carnivorous' describe a way of life. Most members of the Carnivora are indeed carnivorous, although the bamboo-eating giant panda (*Ailuropoda melanoleuca*) is yet another biological exception. On the other hand, there are many carnivorous animals that are not members of the mammalian order Carnivora.

Each order is divided into a number of *families*. Within the order Carnivora, domestic cats and dogs are classified into two different families (the Felidae and the Canidae, respectively) which exist alongside six others (including the bear family, the Ursidae).

Finally, we come to the two levels of classification which together form the basis of each species' binomial (or 'two part') scientific label, the **genus** (plural: genera) (pronounced 'jean-us' or 'jen-us', and 'jen-er-ah', respectively) and the **species**. *Felis* is one of four genera within the Felidae; the genus contains 31 species, including *F. catus* and the wild cat (*F. silvestris*). *Canis* is one of 16 genera within the Canidae, which contains nine species, including *C. familiaris* and the wolf (*C. lupus*). Some of the issues surrounding organisms' scientific labels are considered in Box 4.1, *The use of organisms' scientific labels*.

Box 4.1   The use of organisms' scientific labels

The main reason why every organism is given a scientific label is to facilitate international communication within the scientific community. Thus, a scientist might have carried out some research and published a paper with the title 'Beziehungen zwischen Hunden (*Canis familiaris*) und Katzen (*Felis catus*) im Rahmen vom Stadtmilieu'. Even if she or he was unable to read German, any other scientist could immediately see that the paper concerned two particular animal species. If those species were relevant to the scientist's own work, translation of the paper's title and summary, and then perhaps the entire paper, could be arranged. But without the use of species' scientific labels in this way, comparatively few scientists would realize the potential relevance of papers written in languages other than their own.

To help you become familiar with the use of organisms' scientific labels, we use them in this block just as you might come across them in scientific papers. Where an organism has a widely used common name, its scientific label is usually given in parentheses the first time the species is referred to, but not used thereafter. Where several species belong to the same genus, the genus is often abbreviated, after the first use, to just its initial letter followed by a full stop, provided there is no ambiguity, e.g. 'the domestic horse (*Equus caballus*) and the donkey (*E. asinus*)'. If a species

does not have a common name (e.g. the common gut bacterium, *Escherichia coli*), its scientific label has to be used throughout (abbreviated to *E. coli* after first use). Where an author wishes to refer to all the species in a genus (or cannot distinguish between species), then the genus label is used by itself and *never* abbreviated to just its initial letter, e.g. the fly genus *Drosophila*.

Doubtless you will have noticed that the scientific labels of genera (whether abbreviated or not) and species are always printed in *italics*. If possible (e.g. when using a word processor), you should use italics for genera and species labels. If this is not possible (e.g. in handwriting), you should underline the labels. Thus, '*Felis catus*' and 'Felis catus' are equally acceptable; however, 'Felis catus' and '*Felis catus*' are forms that should be avoided. Note that the names of genera always start with a capital letter, as do those of families, orders, classes, etc. However, the names of species *never* do, even when the species has been named after a person (e.g. Bonelli's warbler, *Phylloscopus bonelli*). It is surprising how often scientific labels are used incorrectly in newspapers or magazines.

Finally, you may have noticed that gardeners use 'scientific-looking' names for plants. Beware! Sometimes the names used really are the species' scientific labels. However, there are many exceptions. For instance, plants that gardeners call 'geraniums' belong to the genus *Pelargonium*; on the other hand, *Geranium* is the scientific label of the genus which includes bloody crane's-bill (*G. sanguineum*).

Question 4.2 Figure 4.9 shows how *F. catus* can be 'nested' within successively broader, more inclusive, levels of classification. Produce a similar diagram for *C. familiaris*. ◀

Activity 2.2 (continued) **Your glossary of biological terms**

You should think about what new terms it is appropriate to add to your glossary. While there is no need to add all the species labels mentioned in the text, you might choose to record a few (such as that of our own species). ◀

Activity 4.2 **Working with a scheme of biological classification**

In this activity you will develop your understanding of biological classification through working with information on primates. ◀

4.4 Summary of Section 4

While, in principle, species can be defined on the basis of their reproductive isolation from other species, in practice species are more usually recognized on the basis of their physical (and sometimes behavioural) features.

Species are placed within a scheme of classification which biologists believe reflects the course of evolution.

At the broadest level of classification, species can be placed in one of three domains: the Archaea and Bacteria (prokaryotes that are mostly unicellular); and the Eukarya (unicellular or multicellular eukaryotes). The domain Eukarya is further divided into four kingdoms: the Protoctista (protoctists — mostly unicellular eukaryotes); the Fungi (fungi — mostly multicellular heterotrophic eukaryotes); the Plantae (plants — mostly multicellular autotrophic eukaryotes); and the Animalia (animals — multicellular heterotrophic eukaryotes).

The kingdoms are divided into about 100 phyla. In the animal kingdom each phylum represents a different fundamental body plan.

An organism's binomial scientific label, which is important for international scientific communication, is a combination of its genus and species labels (e.g. that for modern humans is *Homo sapiens*).

You are expected to remember the *names* of the three domains (i.e. Archaea, Bacteria and Eukarya) and the four eukaryotic kingdoms (i.e. Protoctista, Fungi, Plantae and Animalia, or their informal alternatives). You are also expected to remember only those *levels* within the classification scheme that are printed in bold (i.e. domain, kingdom, phylum, genus and species). (If you do want to commit to memory all the levels from kingdom to species, you might find it helpful to use a mnemonic, such as 'King Philip calmly ordered fried green snakes'!). You are not expected to remember the scientific labels of any particular species.

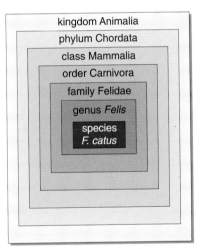

Figure 4.9 Diagram to show how *F. catus* can be 'nested' within successively broader levels of classification.

5 Biodiversity

The word 'biodiversity' is widely used these days, by biologists, in the popular media and even by politicians. It is, however, rarely defined clearly. Most commonly, **biodiversity** refers to the fact that the Earth contains a very large number of animal, plant and other species, and that these species are extremely diverse in size, appearance and behaviour. You will recall from Section 4 that our classification scheme was devised partly to help us cope with biodiversity in this sense. Sometimes the word is also used to encompass the diversity of ecological systems.

Since biologists have been carefully documenting the Earth's living organisms for many years, it may well come as a surprise to you to learn that we remain quite ignorant about how many species there are. The basic problem is that there are so many species on Earth that biologists have barely begun the task of documenting them. A secondary problem is that no central archive exists, so that we even have to estimate the number of species that have been recorded and labelled. Approximately 1.5 million living species have been described in detail (Box 5.1, *The number of living species*).

Box 5.1   *The number of living species*

According to the American biologist Edward O. Wilson, in his book *The Diversity of Life* (1992), about 1 413 000 species have been fully described, labelled and classified. Of these, 73% are animals and 18% are plants.

Within the animal kingdom, arthropods have by far the largest number of species (Table 5.1).

Table 5.1   Numbers of species in the different animal phyla.

Animal phyla	Number of species
Arthropoda (e.g. insects)	874 400
Mollusca (e.g. snails)	50 000
Chordata (e.g. fishes, amphibians, reptiles, birds, mammals)	42 300
Platyhelminthes (e.g. tapeworms)	12 200
Nematoda (i.e. unsegmented worms)	12 000
Annelida (i.e. segmented worms)	12 000
Cnidaria and Ctenophora (e.g. jellyfish)	9 000
Echinodermata (e.g. starfish)	6 100
Porifera (e.g. sponges)	5 000
other phyla, each with relatively few species	9 300

Within the arthropod phylum, the insect class is the largest and, within that class, the beetle order predominates (Table 5.2).

Table 5.2 Numbers of species within sub-groups of the phylum Arthropoda.

Arthropod classes	Number of species
class Insecta	
order Coleoptera (beetles)	290 000
order Lepidoptera (butterflies, moths)	112 000
order Hymenoptera (ants, bees)	103 000
order Diptera (two-winged or true flies)	98 500
orders Homoptera and Hemiptera (true bugs)	82 000
other insect orders	65 500
class Arachnida (e.g. spiders)	73 400
other arthropod classes	50 000

No wonder the British biologist J. B. S. Haldane (1893–1964), on being asked what one could conclude as to the nature of the Creator from a study of creation, famously responded 'An inordinate fondness for beetles'!

Documenting the Earth's plants and animals is the fundamental activity of a branch of biology called *taxonomy*. The first taxonomist, the Swedish biologist Linnaeus (Figure 5.1), described 9 000 species of animals and plants. Since then, our knowledge of various groups of organisms has advanced at different rates. The two best-documented groups are birds and mammals, whose current totals are about 9 000 and about 4 000 species, respectively.

There are two major ways that new species are discovered. Some discoveries arise from exploration of parts of the world that have not previously been explored, revealing organisms that are quite new to science. For example, multitudes of small nematodes (unsegmented worms) have recently been found in previously unsampled oceanic sediments. Other new species are animals and plants that have been known for some time, but not differentiated from very similar species. As recently as 1996, the British pipistrelle bat (*Pipistrellus pipistrellus*) was divided, initially on the basis of differences in the very high frequency calls they use for navigation, into two distinct species known as the brown pipistrelle and the bandit pipistrelle (which, at the time of writing, have not yet been given new scientific labels). Many species are very similar to one another and can only be distinguished on the basis of detailed research which takes a long time to complete. For birds and mammals, discoveries of new species are now rare, but they continue to be made for less well-known groups such as insects. Thus, while it is estimated that the world inventory of bird species now increases by only about 0.05 species per year (i.e. one new species every 20 years) on average, those for insects, arachnids, fungi and nematodes, are increasing by an average of 0.8, 1.8, 2.4 and 2.4 species per year, respectively. In other words, for every new bird species described, biologists are finding about 50 new species each of fungi and nematodes.

Figure 5.1 Carolus Linnaeus (1707–1778), as he is usually known (although originally called Carl Linné and later ennobled as Carl von Linné), was the first taxonomist. He described 9 000 species of animals and plants in the tenth edition of his book *Systema Naturae* (1758). As well as cataloguing many species for the first time, Linnaeus also devised the system of classification and binomial labelling of species described in Section 4.

5.1 Estimating species numbers

While the number of species already documented and described is known with *reasonable* accuracy, the *total* number of living species can only be estimated. Such estimates are made using simple arguments, based on the relative abundances of organisms already known, and a variety of assumptions, the validity of which may be open to question. Thus, while the estimates are useful for getting an indication of the numbers involved, the results obtained should be treated with caution.

To take one example of such an estimate, the catalogues of known bird and mammal species indicate that for both these fairly completely-described groups, there are twice as many species living in the tropics as in temperate regions of the Earth. In contrast, most insect species that have been described so far are from temperate regions. On the assumption that insects, like birds and mammals, are in reality twice as numerous in the tropics, it has been estimated that the Earth contains 3–5 million insect species.

● For which groups of organisms do you suppose that estimates of species numbers are most likely, and least likely, to be accurate?

○ The estimates are most likely to be accurate for birds and mammals. Since new species are only rarely described for these groups, it appears that most species have already been described (which is hardly surprising, given that most are fairly conspicuous). It is for groups like insects, arachnids and nematodes, in which the rates at which new species are still being discovered are relatively high, that there is greatest uncertainty about how many species there are altogether.

One technique used to estimate species numbers is to sample a new region of the world and determine the proportion of species in the sample that have already been described.

Question 5.1   Bugs are members of two insect orders (Table 5.2). A study of bugs in Indonesia revealed 1 690 species, of which 63% were new to science. Assuming that the percentage of previously unknown bug species is similar throughout the world, use information from Table 5.2 to estimate the total number of bug species on Earth. ◀

A study of beetles in Panama by the American biologist Terry Erwin used similar methods to estimate the total number of arthropod species living in the world's tropical forests. Erwin and his team blew a fog of fast-acting insecticide from ground-level into the tops of individual trees at dawn when there was very little wind. For the next five hours they collected the 'rain' of dead and dying arthropods in funnels arranged beneath the trees. Finally, the specimens were sorted and sent to specialists for identification. Erwin found that 163 species of beetle lived *exclusively* in the crowns of *one* species of tree that he considered to be typical of the tropics.

● Using Erwin's estimate that beetles represent about 40% of all described arthropods, roughly how many arthropod species inhabit only the crowns of this particular species of tree?

○ $163 \times (100\%/40\%)$, or about 400 species.

● Erwin reckoned that there are about 5×10^4 species of tropical tree. He also believed that most arthropod species are confined to single tree species. Roughly how many species of arthropod live in the crowns of tropical trees?

About $400 \times 5 \times 10^4$, i.e. about 2×10^7 species.

Finally, Erwin reckoned that about half as many arthropod species live on the ground as in the crowns of tropical trees. What would be his total for the number of arthropod species inhabiting tropical forests?

About 10^7 species live on the ground (half of 2×10^7), so the total number of species would be about $2 \times 10^7 + 10^7$, i.e. 3×10^7.

Question 5.2   One of the problems of estimating species numbers in these sorts of way is that quite a few assumptions have to be made. What do you consider to be the six most important assumptions made by Erwin? ◀

Another method that has been used to estimate species numbers is based on the fact that organisms vary in body size and that larger organisms are less numerous than smaller ones. As a general rule, a ten-fold reduction in body size between one group of species and another group usually means that the smaller species will be 100 times more numerous than the larger. For obvious reasons, biologists probably know most of the world's larger species, so their numbers can be estimated quite accurately. From the number of large animals already documented, it has been estimated by this method that there is a total of 10^7 species of land-dwelling animals. This is in marked contrast to Erwin's estimate.

It should now be clear that making estimates of the number of living species is a very imprecise process, which depends on assumptions that may or may not be true. It is thus not surprising that such estimates vary enormously, between about 10 and 100 million. The figure of 30 million species is widely accepted as the best estimate at present.

Activity 5.1   Extracting information from a scientific article

In this activity you will practise extracting information on a particular topic — in this case biodiversity — from a scientific article. ◀

5.2   Species turnover

Current popular and scientific interest in biodiversity has arisen primarily because biodiversity on Earth is seriously threatened. We live at a time when plant and animal species are becoming extinct at a very high rate, as the direct or indirect result of human activities. However, the extinction of species is not a recent phenomenon. Extinction is an integral part of the evolutionary process and it has been occurring ever since life on Earth began to evolve. Nor can extinction be regarded as a rare or unusual event; indeed, it is the fate of most species to become extinct and the vast majority that have ever existed are now extinct. The 30 million or so species alive today are believed to represent only a tiny fraction of the total number that have existed since life began on Earth.

Evolution is a process of change, in which new species are constantly appearing, and older species are disappearing. Thus, there has always been a turnover of species on Earth. However, the rate at which this turnover has occurred has not been constant over time; it has been *much* faster during certain periods of the Earth's history than during others. These periods of accelerated species turnover, called *mass extinctions*, are discussed in Block 10. In the view of many biologists, we are currently witnessing a mass extinction event caused by human activity in which the rate of

Figure 5.2 Ammonites were abundant in the sea for hundreds of millions of years and are often found as fossils. They became extinct about 65 Ma ago.

species extinction is so high that it is likely to have a more profound effect on the Earth's biodiversity than *any* of the previous mass extinctions.

It is largely from the study of fossils that we know what we do about life on Earth in the past, and hence can make some kind of estimate of former rates of species turnover. The fossil record contains an even more diverse range of organisms than the variety of living species. Some fossil remains are of species that bear little or no resemblance to living species, whereas others clearly resemble living species and may be their evolutionary ancestors. An important distinction must therefore be made between the true extinction of a species, representing the 'end of the line' for that species (or even a whole group of species if it leaves no descendent species), and the gradual replacement over time of one species by a descendent species. Ammonites (Figure 5.2) are an example of the 'end of the line', since they appear to have left no descendants when they became extinct 65 Ma ago. On the other hand, although the dinosaurs are usually thought of as having become extinct at the same time, this may not be strictly true, as living birds probably descended from a group of related reptiles. One of the features of the era of rapid extinction that we are currently witnessing is that the species that are becoming extinct are not leaving descendent species.

Attempts have been made to estimate the number of species in various groups of organisms that have inhabited the Earth, and thus to arrive at a figure for the average time for which individual species exist. Given the fact that there is considerable variation in estimates of the number of living species, it is not surprising that estimates of species longevities, from origin to extinction, are very vague indeed. For example, estimates of the number of bird species that have existed on Earth since the time of one of the earliest known fossil species, *Archeopteryx*, about 125 Ma ago, range from 1.5×10^5 to 1.6×10^6. While these estimates are wildly different, both suggest that the 9 000 or so species of birds estimated to be alive today represent only a very small proportion of the total number of species that have existed. From figures such as these, it has been estimated that the average longevity of a bird species is about half a million years. A similar figure has been estimated for mammals. However, average species longevities are believed to be much longer for most other animal groups. Why species turnover rates should be higher for birds and mammals than for other groups of animals is a question that biologists have not yet been able to answer.

Incidentally, 'modern' *Homo sapiens* certainly existed 100 000 years ago and 400 000-year-old fossils have been found of what has been called 'archaic *Homo sapiens*'. However, considerable controversy surrounds all aspects of the origin and evolution of humans, with new information becoming available at frequent intervals.

5.3 Why does biodiversity matter?

Biodiversity on Earth is threatened because innumerable animal, plant and other species are being driven to extinction by the destruction of their natural habitats, hunting, pollution and a number of indirect effects of human activities. These processes are generated by the needs of a rapidly expanding human population for resources, primarily space in which to live and land on which to grow food. These effects are exacerbated by the market-driven economies of the developed world, which exploit the whole world for the raw materials needed to make a wide range of products. Among the arguments that have been advanced against this over-exploitation of the Earth's resources are those based on ethics, on aesthetics, on biology and even on economics.

Every extinction represents the loss of a species that can never be re-created. Even more importantly, it may be symptomatic of a profound destabilization of the Earth's ecology, the long-term effects of which cannot be predicted. There are many who argue that the reduction of biodiversity will eventually threaten the continued existence of the human species. For example, deforestation is helping to alter the composition of the Earth's atmosphere (Block 2, Section 8.7.1), a process which, if not checked, threatens all forms of life. Pollution is causing a thinning of the ozone layer in the upper atmosphere, exposing the Earth's surface to increasing levels of ultraviolet radiation which is harmful to living things (Block 3, Section 18.2). Finally, humans are largely dependent on other living species as sources of food and medicines and we simply do not know what vital resources may be lost when species become extinct. As ecologist Robert May, at the time of writing Chief Scientific Adviser to the UK Government, put it in 1992:

> … utilitarian reasons for counting and cataloguing species are also noteworthy. A considerable fraction of modern medicines has been developed from biological compounds found in plants. Society would be well advised to keep looking at other shelves in the larder rather than destroying them. Many nutritious fruits and root crops remain largely unexploited; cultivating them could expand and improve the global food supply.

5.4 Summary of Section 5

Biodiversity refers to the very large number of animal, plant and other species, and to their very great diversity.

There are estimated to be between 10 and 100 million (about 30 million being a widely accepted figure) species alive at the present time, of which at least 3–5 million are insects.

The vast majority of species that have ever lived are now extinct, only some having left descendent species.

The average longevity of bird and mammal species may be about half a million years, but the average species longevity is probably much greater in most other animal groups.

Many biologists believe that, as a consequence of habitat destruction, pollution, etc. caused by humans, the current rate of species extinction is comparable with the highest rates detectable in the fossil record (i.e. during so-called mass extinctions).

Loss of biodiversity matters for ethical, aesthetic, biological and economic reasons.

6 Reproduction

In our everyday lives we measure success in a variety of different ways, for instance by whether we win a race, get selected for a job or pass an examination. In biology **success** is measured by the number of descendants an organism leaves. The more descendants it leaves, the more successful it has been. Organisms which inhabit the Earth today — humans included — are all descended from successful ancestors.

In order to leave descendants in the long term, an organism has to produce offspring. You should recall from Section 2 that the production of offspring (i.e. reproduction) is one of the three attributes of life. However, reproduction is just the first stage in leaving descendants. The offspring have to reproduce, as do their offspring and so on for generation after generation.

Essentially there are two ways in which organisms can reproduce. They can do so alone, out of their own resources, in what is called asexual reproduction, or they can do so with another organism of the same species, in what is called sexual reproduction. Each of these ways has advantages and disadvantages, some of which are discussed here.

6.1 Asexual reproduction

When a cell divides by mitosis it produces two identical progeny cells (Section 3.3). Of crucial importance here is the fact that the DNA each progeny cell contains is an identical copy of that of the parent cell. The two progeny cells, which contain identical DNA, are referred to as **clones**. In unicellular organisms (i.e. most prokaryotes and protoctists), these two progeny cells would be two new organisms. In multicellular organisms, cell division leads to growth; the organisms consist of more and more cells, and so get bigger. The point is that all the cells in multicellular organisms are clones of the original zygote. If some of those cells are used to produce a new organism, then that new organism is often referred to loosely as a 'clone' of the original organism. Box 6.1, *A clone called Dolly*, describes the first cloning of an adult mammal.

> ### Box 6.1 A clone called Dolly
>
> Dolly, the cloned sheep, was introduced to the world in February 1997. What makes Dolly special is that she was cloned from another sheep. Scientists in Scotland took an ovum (i.e. an unfertilized egg) from a ewe (sheep 1) and discarded its nucleus. At the same time, they extracted the nucleus from a cell taken from the udder of another ewe (sheep 2). They then inserted the nucleus from sheep 2 into the ovum cell from sheep 1, thus producing the equivalent of a zygote. Floating in a liquid designed to support metabolism, this cell was allowed to undergo several mitotic divisions before the resulting cluster of cells (or *embryo*) was placed in the uterus of a third sheep, the surrogate mother. Five months later Dolly was born. Although the scientists attempted the process 277 times, Dolly was their only complete success.
>
> ● Is Dolly best described as a clone of the donor of the ovum, a clone of the donor of the nucleus, or a clone of the surrogate mother?

Dolly is best described as a clone of the donor of the nucleus. This is because all the DNA in the nuclei of all her cells is identical to the DNA in the donated nucleus as a consequence of repeated mitotic cell division.

Before leaving Dolly, we ought to sound a word of caution. While Dolly's nuclear DNA is certainly cloned from the donated nuclear DNA, the cytoplasm of the 'zygote' came from the ovum donor. Therefore, it was not truly a clone of either original cell. Moreover, as Dolly developed in a different environment to both these donors — in the uterus of the surrogate mother — she would not be expected to be identical to either.

Some multicellular organisms are able to direct cell division so as to produce a new organism 'on the side' (often literally). This type of reproduction, in which an organism reproduces on its own, is known as **asexual reproduction**. Asexual reproduction is illustrated here with the strawberry plant, *Fragaria ananassa* (Figure 6.1).

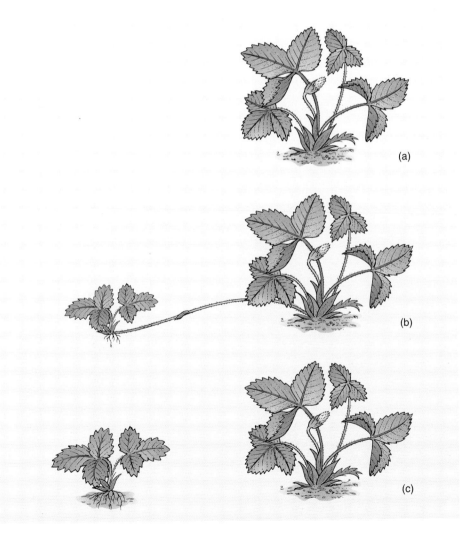

(a)

(b)

(c)

Figure 6.1 Asexual reproduction in the strawberry (*Fragaria ananassa*). (a) A mature parent plant. (b) The same parent plant showing a runner and a developing plant. (c) The runner has now disappeared, leaving the parent plant and the asexually produced offspring.

Figure 6.2 A species of bamboo (*Phyllostachys pubescens*). Bamboo is a kind of grass which reproduces in much the same way as the strawberry, except that bamboo runners are much fatter, run underground and each one can produce several new plants.

During asexual reproduction, the mature strawberry plant produces long, thin shoots called runners. The runners grow out from all sides of the plant keeping close to, but just above, the ground. When a runner is 5–10 cm long, leaves begin to form at its end (Figure 6.1b). These leaves will eventually be part of a new plant. The runner keeps growing away from the parent plant, but the longer it gets, the less able it is to keep the new leaves at its tip above the ground. So, when the runner is 10–15 cm long, it sags sufficiently for the tip to come into contact with the ground. When such contact is made, roots grow down into the soil. The roots and leaves at the tip of the runner are not a new plant yet, because they remain connected to the parent plant by the runner. However, once the roots have become established, the runner joining the parent to its offspring withers and breaks, leaving two separate plants (Figure 6.1c). The original plant has reproduced.

○ Is the new strawberry plant, formed at the end of a runner, a clone of the parent plant?

○ The new strawberry plant is indeed a clone of the parent. The cells of the new plant arose by mitosis of cells in the parent plant and so contain identical DNA to that in the cells of the parent plant.

Many plants use asexual reproduction and some of these produce clones which cover vast areas. For instance, the bamboo forests of China (Figure 6.2) originate in this way.

Asexual reproduction is not restricted to plants. The tiny, soft-bodied, pond-dwelling animal *Hydra* can also reproduce asexually. The cells on the trunk of *Hydra* sometimes divide in such a way as to form a bud on the side of the trunk (Figure 6.3). The bud grows out from the side of the parent animal until it becomes a small, but complete, version of the parent. Once fully formed, the offspring separates from the parent.

Figure 6.3 Asexual reproduction through budding in *Hydra* (magnification ×5).

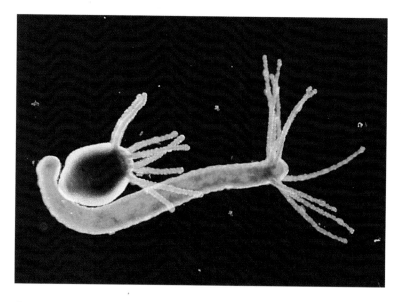

○ Is the new *Hydra*, formed by budding, a clone of the parent plant?

○ The new *Hydra* is indeed a clone of the parent. Its cells arose by mitosis of cells in the parent and so contain identical DNA to that in the cells of the parent animal.

The advantage of asexual reproduction is that it allows the DNA of a successful organism to be passed on intact to its offspring. This is a good strategy and lots of organisms use it. However, many organisms do not use asexual reproduction but instead go in for sexual reproduction.

Question 6.1   (a) What is the main consequence of asexual reproduction?

(b) Why might you expect an asexually produced offspring to be successful? ◀

6.2 Sexual reproduction

As noted earlier, **sexual reproduction** requires the involvement of two individual organisms belonging to the same species. Each produces special types of cell, called gametes, which fuse together to form a zygote from which the offspring grows (Section 3.2). We begin by outlining the type of cell division that results in the production of gametes.

The only type of cell division that we have considered so far is that which involves mitosis.

 What does mitosis ensure in terms of chromosomes?

It ensures that each progeny cell contains chromosomes that are exact copies of those of the parent cell in every respect.

There is a second type of cell division, involving a process known as *meiosis* (pronounced 'my-oh-sis'), which ensures that each progeny cell contains exactly *half* the chromosomes of the parent cell.

In humans, how many chromosomes would there be in a progeny cell produced by meiosis?

Since human cells normally contain 46 chromosomes, there should be 23 chromosomes in a progeny cell produced by meiosis.

In fact, the progeny cells do not contain just *any* 23 of the 46 original chromosomes. Recall that human cells are diploid, containing 22 pairs of autosomes and two sex chromosomes (Section 3.2). The progeny cells contain one member of each of the 22 pairs of autosomes plus one of the two sex chromosomes. In order to achieve this very precise outcome, the process of meiosis is rather more elaborate than that of mitosis. However, here we are concerned only with the results of meiosis rather than its details.

The cells produced by meiosis, which contain one sex chromosome and one member of each pair of autosomes, are said to be **haploid** rather than diploid. Some organisms (e.g. some fungi, algae and insects) spend a fair part of their life cycle with all their cells in the haploid state. Other organisms (e.g. mammals) use haploid cells only for sexual reproduction. In such sexually reproducing organisms, haploid cells constitute an extremely special group because only haploid cells directly contribute DNA to the next generation. The haploid cells are called **ova** (each one being an *ovum*, sometimes called an egg) in female animals and **spermatozoa** (or sperm, for short; each one being a *spermatozoon*) in male animals. The equivalent terms in plants are *ovules* and *pollen grains*. Collectively, the haploid cells involved in reproduction are known as **gametes**.

Sexual reproduction requires that a sperm fuses with (or *fertilizes*) an ovum. Although some animal, and many plant, species are hermaphrodite (i.e. they produce both male and female gametes), the sperm and ova must usually come from different individuals if fertilization is to occur. Moreover, those two individuals must usually be of the same species. If they are not, then either fertilization will not occur at all or the resulting hybrid offspring will have much reduced fertility (Section 4.1).

When a sperm fertilizes an ovum, the result is a single cell called a **zygote** (this is a more accurate definition and replaces that given in Section 3.2). After fertilization, the chromosomes present in the sperm and those present in the ovum are brought together in the zygote.

● Is the zygote haploid or diploid?

○ The zygote is diploid. The zygote contains a haploid set of chromosomes from the sperm and a haploid set from the ovum, making a diploid set of chromosomes in all.

The strawberry plant, which was used to illustrate asexual reproduction (Section 6.1), also reproduces sexually. In sexual reproduction, the plant produces flowers, which are really quite complex structures (Figure 6.4). Some strawberry plants have flowers that produce both ovules and pollen grains. Others have only either female (i.e. ovule-producing) flowers or male (i.e. pollen-producing) flowers. Whatever the precise arrangement, fertilization requires that a pollen grain from one flower gets to the ovule of another flower. The pollen is carried from one flower to another attached to the body of an insect (such as a bee). Even if a pollen grain gets carried to a flower of the same species, it may not fertilize an ovule. Only pollen that attaches to a particular small part of the flower, the stigma, will do so (Figure 6.4b). Soon after it arrives on a stigma, a pollen grain grows a tube down to the ovule. The pollen nucleus moves down the tube to enter the ovule. The resulting zygote grows into a seed by repeated mitotic divisions. The seed of the strawberry is very small (Figure 6.4c) and is usually seen on the outside of the familiar 'fruit' (Figure 6.4d). The seed may eventually grow into a new individual plant, provided it encounters favourable conditions. The complete sexual reproduction cycle of the strawberry is shown in Figure 6.5.

Figure 6.4   (a) The flower of the strawberry plant. (b) The flower of the strawberry plant, cut in half and magnified to show the detail. (The petals have been removed.) (c) The seed of the strawberry plant. (d) Seeds on the surface of the strawberry 'fruit'.

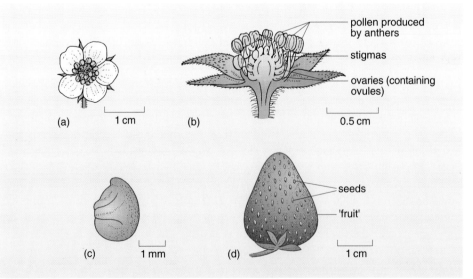

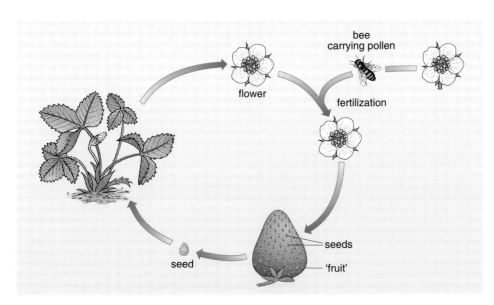

Figure 6.5 Sexual reproduction cycle in the strawberry.

Activity 6.1 Drawing a flow diagram

This activity asks you to draw a flow diagram showing, at the cellular level, the sequence of events in sexual reproduction described in the text. ◀

It is clear that, compared to asexual reproduction, sexual reproduction in plants is much more complex, involving specialized organs (i.e. flowers) and cells (i.e. ovules and pollen grains). It also involves the wasteful business of getting pollen from one flower to the stigma of another. For animals the problems of getting sperm into contact with ova are no less complex. Some animals (e.g. many fishes) use water to carry their gametes. When a male is near to a female of the same species, they squirt their respective sperm and ova into the water so that there is *external* fertilization. On the other hand, most land-based animals, including insects, birds and mammals, require the male to squirt sperm into the female so that fertilization is *internal*. Just how risky such mating can be is illustrated by spiders. Male spiders are usually smaller than females of the same species. In order to mate, the male has to climb on to the female whereupon he is in grave danger of being eaten!

We have seen that sexual reproduction has a number of disadvantages over asexual reproduction. Yet sexual reproduction is used by many species. An important question taxing the minds of contemporary biologists is 'what is so advantageous about sexual reproduction that so many organisms use it?'. Although the answer remains unclear at present, there is likely to be great significance in the fact that DNA from two individuals is combined in the offspring to produce a different combination of chromosomes than in either parent.

Question 6.2   Select *six* words from the following list and use each selected word *once* to correctly complete sentences (a) and (b): meiosis, mitosis, haploid, diploid, spermatozoon, ovum, pollen, stigma, zygote.

(a) A male _____ fertilizes a female _____ to produce a _____ _____ .

(b) Gametes are _____ and are produced by cell division which involves _____ .

Question 6.3   (a) Why should the term 'zygote' not be used in connection with asexual reproduction?

(b) Why is the zygote not a clone of the male contributing the sperm in sexual reproduction? ◀

Activity 2.2 (continued)   Your glossary of biological terms

You should add terms as appropriate to your glossary. ◀

Activity 6.2   Comparing sexual and asexual reproduction

In this activity you will draw up a table to compare the characteristics of sexual and asexual reproduction. ◀

6.3   Summary of Section 6

The more descendants an organism leaves, the more successful it has been.

Asexual reproduction leads to the production of offspring whose chromosomes are identical to one another and to those of their parent; they are clones.

In sexual reproduction, half the male parent's chromosomes are combined with half the female parent's chromosomes to produce offspring with a different combination of chromosomes.

Gametes (i.e. ova and sperm in animals; ovules and pollen grains in plants) are haploid, containing unpaired chromosomes. When gametes fuse at fertilization, the resulting zygote is diploid and contains paired autosomes plus a sex chromosome from each parent (where sex is determined in this way, e.g. in humans).

Sexual reproduction is complex, wasteful and can be risky compared to asexual reproduction. There must therefore be some compensating advantage, probably related to DNA from two individuals being brought together in their offspring.

Ecology: relationships between species

So far in this block we have been concerned with the individual organism; with what makes it an organism (as opposed to, say, a rock), what distinguishes one organism from another and how many different kinds there might be. Real organisms, though, are parts of communities and populations in which there are complex interactions. In this section we explore the oak tree as a habitat upon (and in) which many organisms of many species live. The oak tree is also part of an ecological system, or *ecosystem*, through which resources flow.

Activity 7.1   Ecological chains: finding the links

This CD-ROM activity introduces you to the study of an oak tree ecosytem. You will study a number of interactions between species in this ecosystem. In doing so you will learn about the interdependence of communities of organisms, sometimes referred to as the balance of nature. ◀

Activity 7.2   The correct use of terminology

This activity will develop your skills in handling scientific terminology, by requiring you to use some of these terms correctly in a piece of writing. ◀

7.1   Summary of Section 7

All the principles applicable to the oak wood ecosystem also apply to any other ecosystem.

Food chains begin with autotrophs.

All organisms are part of several food chains which combine to form a food web.

Food chains can vary with the time of year, but always consist of several trophic levels separated by the consumption (in whole or in part) of one organism by another.

Different organisms have different life cycles which vary in the number of stages, their duration and their location. Each of these stages is a potential food source for other organisms; each of the stages may have different food requirements from other stages.

It is possible to calculate the energy flow through food chains and hence through an ecosystem. This can be done by measuring the amount of energy captured by photosynthesis, accumulated in biomass and lost through respiration in plants, and by measuring the consumption, biomass accumulation and energy lost through respiration and faeces in animals.

An organism's success depends on getting the timing right, in terms of when it reproduces with respect to the availability of a suitable food resource.

8 The biology of populations

Individual winter moth caterpillars (*Operophthera brumata*) eat the leaves of oak trees (*Quercus robur*), but whether or not they cause serious damage to a tree of a particular size depends not only on how many leaves each caterpillar eats, but also on how many caterpillars there are on the tree. It is the size of the caterpillar population, and the factors that affect it, that are important. This section considers some of the factors that affect the population size of organisms.

The term **population** is used in biology to describe a group of individuals belonging to a single species. What actually constitutes a population varies from one study to another; commonly, a particular population is defined in relation to a particular habitat or geographic area. Thus, biologists may study the population of winter moths on a given oak tree, or the population of natterjack toads (*Bufo calamita*) in Britain. Populations may also be defined in terms of a particular property that separates individuals in that population from other members of the species. The category of interest may be adult as opposed to young kestrels (*Falco tinnunculus*), or those badgers (*Meles meles*) that carry tuberculosis. Population is thus a flexible concept, used pragmatically by biologists, depending on the purpose of their study.

8.1 Population size

A study may involve accurately determining the total number of individuals which belong to a defined population, the **population size**. For many purposes, however, seeking an accurate estimate of population size is a waste of time. This is particularly true for small, abundant organisms such as greenfly (*Macrosiphum rosae*). When studying greenfly, biologists are generally interested in the impact that they have on their host plant. This can be assessed by determining the average number present in a specified area or volume: their **population density**. (You may recall a specific use of this term in Block 1, where we referred to the population density of humans in different regions — the number of people per square kilometre — in relation to the availability of water.) It would be possible, though very tedious, to count the total number of greenfly living on a particular rose bush. However, it is much easier, and more useful, to determine their density in terms of, for example, the average number of greenfly on a typical leaf.

If you have greenfly in your garden, you will know that population size is not static. Greenfly are much more abundant at certain times of year than at others, and are more abundant in some years than others. In other words, populations are *dynamic*; they change in size over time. Figure 8.1 illustrates a number of kinds of population dynamics.

Question 8.1   Summarize how the size of each of the populations shown in Figure 8.1 changes over time. (You should describe qualitatively the major trends in the data rather than quoting values of numbers of organisms.) ◀

These three examples illustrate some of the basic features of population size: it may increase, decrease, remain stable, fluctuate irregularly, or display regular cycles. The result of dynamic changes in population size is that a particular species may be common in a locality at one time, but rare at another. The terms 'common' and 'rare' are widely used in everyday language, often in the context of population changes

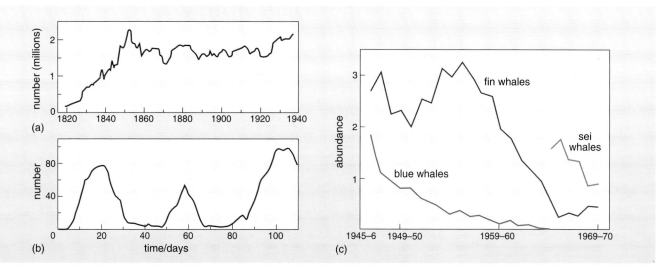

occurring over time, as in the statement 'frogs are less common in Britain than they used to be'. They can also be used to compare the population sizes of different species, as in 'starlings are more common in Britain than kestrels'.

This brings us to a fundamental point about populations of organisms. Even when we take account of the fact that the population size of any one species may fluctuate considerably over time, it is obvious that certain species (e.g. winter moths) are more numerous than others (e.g. sparrowhawks).

Consider a large predator, such as a lion, and suggest two reasons why large predators are rare.

One reason is that predators eat herbivores which in turn eat plants. Between each trophic level, from plants to herbivores to predators, there is very low transfer of energy, so that plants can support only a limited number of herbivores which, in turn, support a smaller number of predators. A second reason is that, being large, individual lions require a large amount of food, so fewer of them can be supported by the available herbivores than if they were small.

There are practical and theoretical reasons why biologists study populations, some of which can be illustrated by considering the examples shown in Figure 8.1. The sheep in Tasmania are farmed for meat and wool. It is important to know the optimum population size to maintain on the island; that is, one that provides a good supply of meat and wool without becoming so large that grass becomes over-grazed, or so small as to become economically inviable. The declining whale populations raise questions about whether these whale species are heading for extinction, about how many whales it is prudent to catch each year and whether the cause of their decline is over-hunting or habitat degradation. These questions are essentially practical ones, relating to the exploitation of other species and their conservation. The fluctuations that occur in many populations, such as the population of water fleas in a laboratory aquarium, raise a more theoretical question: why do many plant and animal populations fluctuate in size over time, even under apparently stable conditions, rather than remain constant?

The two principal events that cause populations to change in size are birth and death. It is therefore necessary to consider some of the issues that influence birth rates and death rates. We will begin by looking at life histories.

Figure 8.1 Change in population size over time. (a) The number of sheep (*Ovis aries*) living in Tasmania. (b) The number of water fleas (*Daphnia*) living in a small aquarium. (c) The abundance of blue (*Balaenoptera musculus*), fin (*B. physalus*) and sei (*B. borealis*) whales, measured as the number caught per 1 000 catcher-days.

8.2 Quantifying life histories

What is meant by the term 'life history'? Individual organisms are born into the world, they grow up, and they struggle to survive in a habitat which, for all or part of the time, has a hostile climate, and which is populated by predators, disease-causing organisms and competitors. Those that do survive to become mature attempt to reproduce and some will be successful, perhaps more than once. Finally comes the inevitability of death. A life history can be described for any given individual in a population, and there is typically a great deal of variation among individuals within a single species in the details of their life histories. Among domestic cats, for example, some individuals live to a great age, others die young; some produce prodigious numbers of kittens, others produce only a few or none at all.

⬤ What distinguishes life histories, as described in the preceding paragraph, from the life cycles you have already studied?

◯ The life history includes what happens to an organism after it has completed the life cycle. The life cycle is a particular, important, part of the life history. {You can see this by referring back to Figure 2.7. The life history would be the life cycle plus one of the two boxes showing the fate of the adult.}

The **life history** is a full schedule of where and when individuals in a species are born, can reproduce and die. This schedule is defined by a number of variables such as: age when first able to reproduce, age at first breeding, interval between *breeding episodes*, number of offspring produced per breeding episode, longevity and therefore potential number of breeding episodes, etc. In many species, the vast majority of individuals die when they are very young. In the common frog (*Rana temporaria*), for example, over 90% of individuals die, many through predation, while still in the egg or tadpole stages. Their life history is very different from the life history shown by those frogs that complete the life cycle, go on to breed 8–10 times and live for 10–12 years.

The diversity that exists among organisms in terms of their life history schedules is further illustrated by plants. Many species, such as groundsel (*Senecio vulgaris*), are *annuals* which grow, produce seed once, and then die, within a single year. Others, called *biennials*, such as the foxglove (*Digitalis purpurea*), also produce seed only once. They typically do not produce flowers in their first year, but then flower and produce seed in their second and final year. Some plants, called *perennials*, produce seed more than once, and may have very high longevities. The North American bristlecone pine (*Pinus cristata*), for example, can live for up to 4 000 years. Among animals there is also considerable variation in longevity, from life histories of a few days for some crustaceans or a few weeks for some insects, to more than 100 years for some of the larger tortoise species.

Longevity is but one aspect of life history. There is also great variation among species in their breeding frequency. Among fishes, for example, the Atlantic salmon (*Salmo salar*) lives for seven years, spawns once and then dies, whereas the Pacific sardine (*Sardinops caerulea*) spawns an average of three times in its ten-year life. A species that breeds only once in its life is said to show **semelparity** (or to be *semelparous*); one that breeds several times shows **iteroparity** (or is *iteroparous*). Long-lived species are typically iteroparous, but this is not always true. A species of bamboo, *Phyllostachys bambusoides*, commonly lives for about 120 years during which time it reproduces only asexually (Section 6.1), before flowering just once and then dying.

Table 8.1 presents data for two life history variables, for a selection of bird species. The mean annual mortality among adults is simply the percentage of adult birds that die each year on average (mortality tends to be *very* much higher among younger birds). The mean expectation of further life reflects the fact that the life expectancy of a bird remains more-or-less constant throughout its adult life unless it survives to a very great age for that species (which *very* few do).

Table 8.1 Annual mortality and life expectancy in some bird species.

Species	Mean annual mortality among adults/%	Mean expectation of further life among surviving adults/y
blue tit (*Parus caeruleus*)	70	0.9
wood pigeon (*Columba palumbrus*)	40	2.0
swift (*Apus apus*)	20	4.5
yellow-eyed penguin (*Megadyptes antipodes*)	10	9.5
royal albatross (*Diomedea epomophora*)	3	32.8

The data presented in Table 8.1 show just some of the diversity that exists within a single class of animals, birds in this instance, in terms of life history variables. They also reveal a common pattern that exists in the life histories of many classes of organisms.

 What overall pattern is revealed by the data in Table 8.1?

The data suggest that species with a high annual mortality have lower life expectancy. That is, as one variable increases the other decreases.

Such a relationship is hardly surprising, but there are other relationships between life history variables that are less obvious. Birds also vary in their schedules of reproduction, for example. The blue tit typically produces one, occasionally two, clutches of about 12 eggs in its short life (1–2 years); a royal albatross may not breed until it is 15 years old, but then produces a single egg every two years throughout its remaining life (which may be up to 80 years).

In general, larger-bodied species are longer-lived and have a slower, iteroparous, reproductive schedule. However, there are exceptions.

 Which species in Table 8.1 fits this generalization least well?

The swift is considerably smaller than the wood pigeon, but it has lower annual mortality and a greater life expectancy.

As you study more biology, you will find that biologists frequently make rather simple generalizations in order to make some sense of the great diversity of species with which they have to deal. As we have already mentioned, however, for virtually every rule or generalization in biology there are exceptions.

Question 8.2   Select from (a)–(j) those attributes which would tend to cause the population of a bird species to increase.

(a) semelparity; (b) low frequency of reproduction; (c) low longevity; (d) high annual mortality; (e) iteroparity; (f) small clutch size; (g) low annual mortality; (h) large clutch size; (i) high longevity; (j) high frequency of reproduction. ◀

8.3 The dynamics of populations

Biologists who study populations have to think in terms of numbers, and of how those numbers change over time. Figure 8.2 represents the growth of a population that has colonized a previously empty habitat, e.g. it could be a plant colonizing a field cleared of its previous vegetation by fire, or goats colonizing an offshore island.

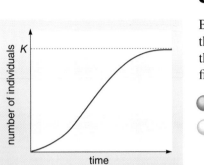

Figure 8.2   Change over time in the size of a population of an organism colonizing a previously empty habitat.

● Describe how the size of the population shown in Figure 8.2 changes over time.

○ The size of the population grows slowly at first (the low gradient means a low rate of change), then increases at an accelerating rate (steep gradients mean higher rates of change) before the growth eventually slows down again (the gradient becomes almost zero). In due course, the population stabilizes at a constant size, labelled K on the graph.

● Suggest why the population grows at an accelerating rate for a while and why it eventually stabilizes at a constant size.

○ The size of the population grows at an accelerating rate because the number of organisms reproducing continues to increase. However, such population growth cannot continue for ever because an inevitable consequence of a larger population size is greater competition for essential resources, so that not all the organisms survive. Eventually, the birth rate and death rate stabilize at equal values and the population ceases to grow.

The curve shown in Figure 8.2 has a distinctive shape and is called a *sigmoidal* or *logistic* curve. This curve depends on two variables that are very important. One variable is a measure of how fast a population can increase (related to the maximum possible rate of reproduction), and is known as the **intrinsic rate of natural increase** of the population, usually designated r. The other is the population's maximum stable size or **carrying capacity**, usually designated K. The variables r and K have numerical values that are specific to particular populations of particular species. Thus, comparing the population growth curves in Figure 8.3, we can say that the values of r and K for population A are different from those of population B.

● Which of the two populations in Figure 8.3 has the higher value of r, and which has the higher value of K?

○ Population A has the higher value of r, as the maximum gradient of its population growth curve (which represents the rate of increase of the population) is greater than that for population B. On the other hand, population B has the higher value of K since its population size has stabilized at a higher level than that for population A.

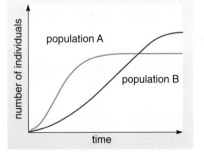

Figure 8.3   Population growth curves for two hypothetical populations, A and B.

Consider a species living in a highly unstable habitat, such as a pond that dries up periodically or an area frequently subject to severe fires. In such circumstances, most of the adult members of the species will be wiped out fairly often.

○ With respect to reproduction, what attributes would tend to maximize the number of descendants that an organism would contribute to the generation which re-colonizes the habitat when conditions improve?

○ It would be advantageous to reproduce at an early age (because any delay might mean there is no opportunity to reproduce at all) and also to produce a large number of offspring (hence increasing the probability that at least one will survive to recolonize the habitat).

Of course, reproducing when young almost certainly means reproducing while still relatively small. Producing lots of progeny (offspring) inevitably means that the progeny themselves will be small and provided with very limited food reserves with which to start their independent existence. Individually, therefore, they have a very low probability of survival. Reaching reproductive maturity comparatively early and then devoting a great deal of energy to the production of lots of progeny means that an organism is likely to reproduce only once or twice in its lifetime. Thus, living in a particular sort of environment provides the impetus for a species to adopt a suite of particular reproductive strategies. Since this suite of strategies is associated with having a relatively high value of r, species adapted to survive in unstable environments are often described as r-species, and their growth and reproductive strategy as an r-strategy.

Now consider a species living in a much more stable, predictable, habitat.

○ What attributes would tend to maximize the number of descendants that an organism would contribute to the generation that eventually takes over from the current adults in a stable habitat?

○ In a stable environment organisms do not need to 'rush into' reproduction, but can afford a reproductive strategy designed to increase the probability of survival of individual progeny. It is likely to be advantageous to live for a long time and grow to a large enough size to compete effectively with other adults for the available resources. It may therefore be better to devote energy to growth rather than to reproduction for some considerable time. When reproductive maturity is eventually reached, it may then be better to breed several, or many, times before death. It may also be better to produce relatively few progeny in each breeding episode, but to provide each one with the necessary resources (e.g. food reserves) to compete well against the progeny of other organisms. This would increase the probability of their survival into adulthood.

Once again, living in a particular sort of environment provides the impetus for a species to adopt a suite of particular reproductive strategies. Since this time the strategies, known as K-strategies, are associated with maintaining the population at or near its carrying capacity, species adapted to flourish in stable environments are often described as K-species.

Generally speaking, a species cannot simultaneously adopt an r-strategy *and* a K-strategy. If it tried to do so in an environment that favoured an r-strategy it would probably lose out to a specialist r-strategist, while in an environment that favoured a K-strategy a specialist K-strategist would probably be better adapted.

We can explore the relationship between r and K, within a species, by considering the simple aquatic organism *Hydra*, which you met briefly in Section 6 and whose life cycle is shown in Figure 8.4. When conditions are good, individual *Hydra* grow to a relatively large size and periodically reproduce asexually, as shown on the right of the

Figure 8.4 The life cycle of *Hydra*.

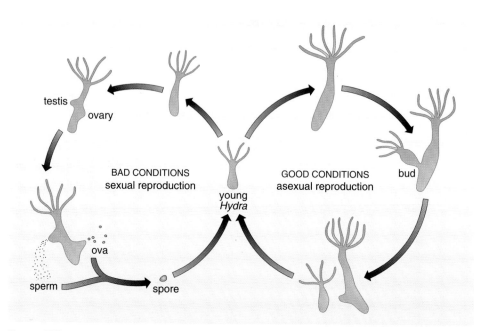

figure. When reproducing asexually, the growth of the parent *Hydra* itself typically slows down or even stops.

⬤ Why do you suppose this happens?

◯ Because the food that previously went into sustaining its own growth is diverted to the developing bud.

An individual *Hydra* can allocate resources primarily to its own growth, or primarily to making a bud; it cannot do both. In other words, there is a trade-off between growth and asexual reproduction. Another trade-off occurs when conditions for *Hydra* start to deteriorate (e.g. its pond starts to dry up in summer). Now, regardless of their size, individual *Hydra* allocate all the resources they can acquire to developing large ovaries and testes which produce huge numbers of ova and sperm that are shed into the water, as shown on the left of Figure 8.4. These gametes fuse with the gametes of other *Hydra* to form zygotes; the zygotes develop into drought-resistant spores which can survive in the ground until conditions improve once again. Here we see a trade-off between growth and sexual reproduction: each individual stops growing and instead puts its resources into making ova and sperm.

⬤ Of the two types of reproduction shown in Figure 8.4, which would you characterize as involving a high value of *K* and which a high value of *r*?

◯ Asexual reproduction in *Hydra* is relatively slow, involving the production of one or two offspring at a time and is thus a *K*-strategy. Sexual reproduction in *Hydra* can potentially produce very large numbers of spores very quickly and is therefore an *r*-strategy.

The concept of a **trade-off** between one aspect of an organism's biology and another is very important in biology, and we shall return to it several times. Consider, by way of analogy, a car. When a car is designed, many conflicting requirements have to be considered, such as comfort, spaciousness, running costs, performance, safety, price, etc. No one model of car can optimize all these things at the same time. To make it more spacious inside means making it less aerodynamic, for example. In other words, the designer makes a trade-off between spaciousness and running costs. Likewise, there must be a trade-off between performance and fuel economy.

We can use the car analogy to make another important point. There are many different kinds of car because different customers have different requirements; these arise because they make different trade-offs when buying a car. A young couple on two incomes with no children to support may prefer a car in which space and fuel economy are sacrificed for elegance and high speed; a few years later, as relatively impoverished parents of several young children, they may value space and economy at the expense of high performance. There are many ways of designing a car; likewise, there are many different ways of being a beetle, a fish or a bird. One of the puzzling questions in biology is why there are so many different types of organism and so many different species. Part of the answer to this question is that there are many different, equally successful, ways of being a particular kind of organism.

Question 8.3   Explain why a bird with a complete set of the five potentially very successful traits listed in Question 8.2 does not exist. ◄

Question 8.4   Explain why each of the following statements is either correct or incorrect:

(a) An organism can display either high r or low r; it cannot display both.

(b) Fishes and frogs are both high K organisms.

(c) It is impossible to estimate the population of the North Sea. ◄

Having considered many of the general principles of population biology, we now turn to a particular species, a small fly called the holly leaf miner, whose population biology you will be studying practically later in the course.

8.4   The holly leaf miner

The adult holly leaf miner (*Phytomyza ilicis*) is a small fly with a body about 1.5 mm long and a wing-span of about 4 mm. Holly leaf miners can be found flying around the branches of many holly bushes and trees (*Ilex aquifolium*) for a few weeks from the end of May each year. However, it is much easier to see the results of young holly leaf miner activity: quite large, rather disfiguring patches on the surface of many of holly leaves (Figure 8.5). Such patches are where the larvae (or grubs) of the fly have chewed their way through the interior of the leaf. Because the larvae feed below the leaf surface, these patches are known as *mines*.

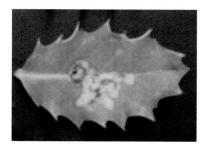

Figure 8.5   A leaf of holly (*Ilex aquifolium*) mined by a larva of the holly leaf miner (*Phytomyza ilicis*).

The adults are semelparous. After mating, the females lay usually one fertilized egg in the central spine (the midrib) of each of up to 100 tender young holly leaves. The eggs quickly hatch into larvae, which feed on the leaves. As the larvae feed, they move along and then away from the midrib, eating into the soft tissue lying between the upper and lower surfaces of the leaves and creating large hollows (the mines). In March, the larvae become pupae. At the end of May, the adults emerge from their pupal cases, and the cycle begins again.

Question 8.5   Make a sketch of the holly leaf miner's life cycle. ◄

○ Would you expect all the fertilized eggs laid by holly leaf miners in one year to give rise to adults capable of reproducing the following year?

○ No. Otherwise the Earth would soon be overrun by holly leaf miners!

In fact, an average of only two of the 100 or so fertilized eggs laid by a female need to become adults that reproduce for the population to remain stable. Death occurs at various points in the holly leaf miner's life cycle, with the result that the huge *potential* population size is reduced to that actually observed in nature. Some eggs fail to hatch. Some larvae and some pupae are killed by tiny parasitic wasps. Some larvae and some pupae are eaten by birds (mainly blue tits). Some adult flies die before mating or before laying eggs. Each of these causes of death is called a **mortality factor**.

From a biologist's point of view, there are two useful things about the holly leaf miner:

1 It is the *only* insect species that creates mines in the leaves of this easily recognized plant species; therefore it is easy to identify.

2 We can examine a mined leaf during the summer months and tell whether an adult emerged successfully (by finding its emergence hole) and, if not, whether it died as a larva or as a pupa, whether it was killed by a parasitic wasp or was eaten by a bird.

It is thus possible to study the life histories of lots of holly leaf miners by examining their mines. In particular, it is possible to quantify the relative importance of each mortality factor and look for changes from year to year or from place to place.

Activity 8.1   Quantifying mortality factors in the holly leaf miner: Part 1

This is the first of two pieces of practical work involving the holly leaf miner. You will undertake the second while you are studying Block 9. The reason for dividing this practical work is that the mines you need to examine will contain holly leaf miners until towards the end of June, and hence cannot be studied until after that date without killing the flies. However, there is much useful preparatory work which can be done now. ◄

We have seen that, in most species, populations have the potential to grow very quickly indeed. On the other hand, a population cannot grow indefinitely, even in a habitat that is initially virtually empty. It follows, therefore, that there is usually quite severe competition for resources within a population. This has important implications for adaptation to the environment and, ultimately, for evolution, as we shall see in the next section.

8.5   Summary of Section 8

A population is a group of individuals belonging to a single species. Sometimes it is the size of a population, and sometimes it is its density, that is of greatest interest.

Populations are dynamic; they may be increasing or decreasing in size, or fluctuating in regular or irregular ways.

Two important characteristics of any population are its intrinsic rate of natural increase (r) and its carrying capacity (K). A distinction can be made between r-strategies and K-strategies; different species tend to adopt one or other of these strategies, but some species can switch from one strategy to the other depending on the environmental conditions.

There are inevitably trade-offs between, for example, growth and reproduction.

Mortality factors act at different points in a species' life history. The holly leaf miner is a very convenient species in which the impact of various mortality factors on a species can be studied quantitatively.

Adaptation and evolution

This section consists of a single activity — a virtual field trip to the Galapagos Islands, which gives you the opportunity to follow in Charles Darwin's footsteps and study the adaptations of some of the animals that live there. Darwin visited the islands in 1835 during his voyage on the *Beagle* and the unique animals and plants that he observed greatly influenced his later thinking on evolution.

Activity 9.1   Galapagos: adaptation and evolution on islands (Part I)

In this CD-ROM activity you will investigate how different species have adapted to their environments in the Galapagos Islands. ◀

9.1   Summary of Section 9

The Galapagos Islands are of great significance to biologists. Many species living in the Galapagos have been studied. These are found to possess characters (adaptations) that suit them for their way of life by increasing the probability that they will survive and reproduce in the environment in which they live.

Darwin's finches illustrate the problems involved in separating different species, using only visible features. The key character that is used to distinguish between Darwin's finch species has great adaptive significance; differences in this key character have a profound influence on the lifestyles adopted by the birds.

10 Evolution through natural selection

So far in this block, we have emphasized that there is a very large number of very diverse species (Section 5) which are nevertheless clearly related to one another (Section 4), and that organisms are generally well adapted to their particular way of life within a specific environment (Sections 7 and 9). These important concepts are linked together by the concept of evolution. The word 'evolution' means 'change over time' and it can be used in relation to anything that has a history; thus, we could describe the evolution of the motor car or of parliamentary democracy. Biological **evolution** refers to the fact that the many organisms that inhabit the Earth today are different from those that existed in the past. The processes that have brought about changes among living organisms are many and varied and one of them, but only one of them, is natural selection.

In this section, we describe the theory of evolution by natural selection as proposed by Charles Darwin (Figure 10.1) in his book, first published in 1859, *On The Origin of Species by Means of Natural Selection, or The Preservation of Favoured Races in the Struggle for Life*. Incidentally, the title of this book, which is generally abbreviated to *The Origin of Species*, is somewhat misleading, as Darwin wrote rather little about how new species are formed, but did write a great deal about adaptation. It is important to note that, at the time when Darwin was writing, there was no knowledge of the mechanism for a crucial aspect of his theory, the passing of characters from parents to offspring. Darwin was aware that inheritance is a fundamental feature of living things, but he had no knowledge of DNA or chromosomes. In this block, we will look at natural selection as Darwin did, taking inheritance for granted, but ignoring the mechanisms underlying it. Later, in Block 9, we will return to natural selection and take another look at the topic, informed by what you will have learned by then about inheritance.

You have almost certainly heard of natural selection before and probably have an idea of what it means. But the way that the term 'natural selection' is often used in newspapers and the like can be misleading. To clarify the scientific meaning, we will begin by describing the theory of natural selection as set out by Darwin, and then consider a specific example of evolution by natural selection.

Figure 10.1 Charles Darwin (1809–1882) briefly studied medicine in Edinburgh before going to Cambridge intending to become an Anglican clergyman. Soon after the voyage of the *Beagle* (1831–1836), during which he was gentleman companion to Captain FitzRoy, Darwin became convinced that biological evolution had occurred *and* saw how it could have been brought about by natural selection. Despite having gathered massive amounts of supporting evidence, Darwin refrained from publishing his revolutionary ideas on evolution for about 20 years until he was almost 'scooped' in 1858 by Alfred Russel Wallace (1823–1913). Darwin continued to live quietly in the country, 'enjoying' ill-health and working on a wide variety of biological problems, as the rest of the world struggled to come to terms with the implications of evolution.

10.1 Darwin and natural selection

While Darwin knew nothing about the mechanism of inheritance, he was very aware of many other aspects of living organisms. Among these, three are particularly emphasized in his theory:

- The species that inhabit the Earth today are not the same species that existed in the past, although they do resemble them. This aspect of evolution was very apparent to Darwin from the fossil record.

- Each species possesses a number of characters that adapt individuals within that species to their way of life and their particular environment. Much of *The Origin of Species* is devoted to detailed descriptions of the adaptations of individual species, for example the various beak shapes of finches on the Galapagos Islands (Section 9).

- Selective breeding of domestic species can produce characters in a diversity of forms. For example, dog breeders have produced numerous breeds that differ in characters such as ear length, stature and behaviour: different breeds have different forms of a character.

Darwin's theory of **natural selection** can be expressed as four propositions. These propositions are so important to an understanding of evolution through natural selection that you should try to remember them, although not necessarily word-for-word.

Darwin's four propositions

1 Within a given species, more individuals are produced by reproduction than can survive within the constraints (e.g. food supply) imposed by the species' environment.

2 Consequently, there is a **struggle for existence**, because of the disparity between the number of individuals produced by reproduction and the number that can survive.

3 Individuals within a species show **variation**; no two individuals are exactly alike (not even those we call 'identical' twins). Those with advantageous characters have a greater probability of survival, and therefore of reproducing, in the struggle for existence.

4 Individuals produce offspring that tend to resemble their parents (the principle of **inheritance**). Provided that the advantageous characters that promote survival are inherited by offspring, individuals possessing those characters will become more common in the population over successive generations because they are more likely than individuals not possessing those characters to survive and produce offspring in the next generation.

The essence of Darwin's theory is that natural selection will occur if three conditions are met. These conditions, highlighted in bold above, are a struggle for existence, variation and inheritance. These are said to be the *necessary and sufficient* conditions for natural selection to occur. To say that the three conditions are *necessary* means that, unless all three conditions are met, natural selection will not occur. Thus, it will not occur if reproduction does not produce more progeny than can survive, it will not occur if a character does not show variation, and it will not occur if variation does not have a heritable basis. To say that the three conditions are *sufficient* means that, if all three conditions are met, natural selection will inevitably occur and this *can* lead to change in the characters of a population from one generation to the next.

Darwin was concerned with evolution, i.e. change over time, and he proposed a process, natural selection, that could bring about such change. Evolution through natural selection is our main focus here. However, it is important to bear in mind that natural selection is also a process that can *prevent* change, i.e. promote stability. In other words, natural selection can occur *without* evolution. Furthermore, there are factors other than natural selection that affect evolution (some of which are considered in Section 10.3). The three conditions listed above are necessary and sufficient for natural selection to occur, rather than for evolution to occur. Nevertheless, the vast majority of biologists accept that *natural selection is the most important process by which evolution is brought about.*

Let us look a little more closely at the three necessary and sufficient conditions and consider how likely it is that they will be met. The first, a struggle for existence, is probably almost always met, because living organisms produce more progeny than are required to replace their parents when they die (recall the holly leaf miner, Section 8.4). The second condition, variation, is often but not always met. Some characters show virtually no variation between members of a species, whilst other characters show considerable variation. The third condition, inheritance, is only sometimes met; not all variation has a heritable basis. For example, toads vary in size. The two factors which make the largest contribution to variation in the body size of toads are variation in age (toads continue to grow throughout their lives) and variation in their environment (e.g. a good food supply). These are both external causes (i.e. body size is not a result of particular characters possessed by the toad). So body size in toads is not primarily an inherited character.

This last point brings us to an important aspect of natural selection, which was much discussed when Darwin first proposed his theory. This debate concerns the possible *inheritance of acquired characters*. As well as growing, individual organisms may develop particular skills or physical characters during the course of their lives as a result of differences in the way they live. Consider the human practices of ear-piercing, circumcision and decorative body scars. These characters, which are acquired deliberately during the course of an individual's life, are not inherited by that individual's offspring even though the practice may have been carried out for hundreds of generations. Likewise, a plant that has grown particularly large in a patch of good ground, or a toad that has grown very big because it lives in a garden full of food, will not pass their large size on to their progeny. So, inheritance of *acquired* characters does not occur.

Inheritance of a character occurs only if that character is passed from one generation to the next during reproduction. In other words, it is reproduction that is the crucial factor in natural selection. In a nutshell, natural selection is about the reproduction — rather than survival — of the fittest. (The term 'fitness' has a very particular meaning in biology, which we will discuss in Section 11.)

10.2 Natural selection in the guppy

The purpose of this section is to consolidate your understanding of the theory of evolution through natural selection by looking at a specific example. The guppy (*Poecilia reticulata*) is a small fish whose natural habitat is small streams in northern Trinidad, but it is also a popular aquarium fish. Male and female guppies are very different in appearance (Figure 10.2); they are said to show sexual dimorphism (Section 4.1) as male guppies are very much more brightly coloured than females. We will consider how natural selection influences bright coloration in male guppies, and we will do so by considering each of Darwin's four propositions in turn.

1 Number of progeny

Female guppies begin to breed as soon as they become mature at about three months old; they then produce clutches of eggs, most of which become fertilized, at roughly one-month intervals until they die or become too old. Clutches vary in size from one to 40 eggs; the average clutch contains about 10 eggs. Thus, female guppies produce a large number of offspring during their lives, far more than can survive to maturity.

Figure 10.2   A variety of guppies produced by selective breeding by aquarists. The two females in the foreground are relatively plain. The four brightly coloured males show variation in the number, size and colour of the spots on their bodies.

Question 10.1   Suppose that, in a particular stream, the size of a population of guppies stays more or less stable over several years. How many of a given female's offspring, on average, must survive to reproductive age in such a population? ◄

Given the large number of fertilized eggs produced by female guppies, and the fact that, on average, only two survive to reproduce, it is clear that there is very high mortality among young organisms in this species. This obviously meets the first of Darwin's propositions. Guppies are fairly typical organisms and illustrate that mortality in nature is typically very high. This mortality provides the background against which natural selection acts.

2   The struggle for existence

During their lives, guppies face a variety of environmental hazards which cause mortality. They must find food and, if food supply is limited, some will die through starvation. Heavy rain periodically causes floods which may wash a large part of a population out to sea; occasional droughts cause populations to perish when streams dry out. Like all organisms, guppies are attacked by a rich variety of parasites and diseases. Of most interest to us in this discussion is that guppies are preyed upon by larger, predatory fishes. Of importance to what follows is the fact that, in their natural habitat, some streams contain many predatory fish, others contain few or none. There is thus variation in the level of predation to which wild populations of guppies are subjected.

3   Variation

Guppies vary in a number of characters; in particular, male guppies vary in the number, size and brightness of the coloured spots that decorate their bodies (Figure 10.2). This variation can be detected within a single population in a given stretch of stream, but is much more obvious when different populations, from different streams, are compared. Biologists working in Trinidad have shown that this variation is related to the presence of predatory fish. Male guppies from streams where predators are absent are much more brightly coloured than those from streams that contain predators.

Question 10.2   Suggest an explanation, in terms of adaptation, for the relationship between the presence or absence of predatory fish in streams and the brightness of male guppies. ◄

As we shall see shortly, the explanation given in the answer to Question 10.2 is supported by other observations. But it does beg an important question: 'why are male guppies brightly coloured at all?' It is quite common among animals that males are more brightly coloured than females (an example of sexual dimorphism; see Section 4.1). The explanation for this is quite complex, but can be summarized briefly. In the majority of animal species, males are the more active partner in initiating mating behaviour and they perform a variety of behaviour patterns to attract the attention of, and stimulate, females. Commonly, females are more effectively attracted and stimulated by the most brightly coloured males, giving such males an advantage in terms of enjoying a higher mating success. For example, peacocks with the greatest number of 'eyespots' in their tails mate with more females than those with fewer eyespots (Figure 4.2b). Likewise, male guppies with more brightly coloured spots are more attractive to females than are those with fewer spots.

The possibility that bright coloration makes male guppies more conspicuous to predators, and the observation that such males are more attractive to females, suggests that the evolution of coloration in male guppies must be seen as an example of a trade-off (Section 8.3). In other words, there is a balance between the advantage that the more brightly coloured males experience in terms of enhanced mating success and the disadvantage they suffer in terms of increased predation risk. Moreover, the point of balance in this trade-off is likely to differ between streams or to shift over time in any one stream, depending on the presence or absence of predators. This example illustrates an important point about trying to explain specific characters of organisms in terms of adaptation. It is not sufficient to explain adaptations just in terms of their apparent advantages. Characters typically also involve costs of some kind and so the actual form of a particular character is the result of a trade-off between costs and benefits.

4   Inheritance

The adaptive explanation for bright coloration in male guppies given above can only be correct, and can only have evolved by natural selection, if male coloration has a heritable basis. Direct evidence that it is a heritable character is of two kinds. First, a wide variety of decorative guppies have been bred for sale on the aquarium market (Figure 10.2). Such forms could not have been produced if male coloration were not heritable. Second, if samples of guppies are taken from different Trinidadian streams and bred in the laboratory, they yield male offspring that resemble their fathers; stocks derived from predator-free streams are more brightly coloured than those from predator-rich streams.

Our discussion so far of the biology of guppies has concentrated on whether the necessary and sufficient conditions for natural selection exist in this species. The fact that they do strongly supports the hypothesis that male coloration has evolved by natural selection. However, this does not constitute a direct, rigorous test of the hypothesis. A series of experiments carried out during the 1970s by the American zoologist John Endler did put the hypothesis to such a test.

In one of his experiments, Endler built several artificial ponds and stocked each with a population of guppies derived from several different localities in Trinidad. At this stage, guppies were the only fish in the ponds. There was considerable variation among males in the number of their spots, but the mean number of spots per male across all the populations at the start of the experiment (time = 0 months) was 10 (Figure 10.3). He left the ponds alone for six months, then sampled the populations in

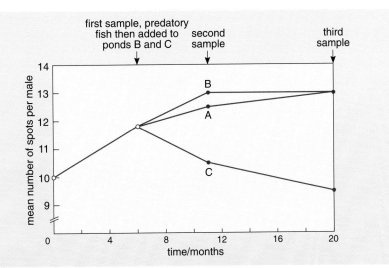

each of the ponds and counted the number of spots on the male guppies. He found that the mean number of spots per male had increased to 11.8 (Figure 10.3).

⬤ What adaptive explanation can you suggest for this increase in male spot number?

◯ In the absence of any predatory fish, natural selection had favoured an increase in spot number. The more heavily spotted males had more offspring because they were more attractive to females.

Six months may well seem a remarkably short period of time for such a change to have come about. Indeed it is, although it is not the actual time that is important. The guppy is iteroparous, and over the course of six months, Endler's artificial populations were able to reproduce several times.

⬤ Why is the number of breeding episodes more significant than the time in months?

◯ Because at each breeding episode females choose the most attractive males with which to mate. The more attractive males, i.e. those that have more spots, father more offspring and as spots are inherited, those offspring have more spots.

Having sampled his populations at six months, Endler divided them into three groups (A, B and C). He added to each group C pond one individual of a fish called *Crenicichla alta*, which is a particularly voracious predator of guppies. To each group B pond he added six individuals of another predatory fish called *Rivulus hartii*, which does not prey on guppies. No fish were added to the group A ponds. The ponds were then left alone for a further five months (time for guppies to breed several more times), at which point he sampled them again and counted the number of spots on the male guppies.

⬤ From Figure 10.3, how did the mean number of spots per male differ between the time of the second sample (at 11 months) and the time of the first sample (at six months) for the three groups of ponds?

◯ The values for groups A and B had increased slightly from 11.8 to 12.5 and 13.0 spots, respectively. However, the value for group C had declined, from 11.8 to 10.5. The populations had therefore diverged in terms of mean male spot number.

In the final phase of his experiment, Endler left his populations for a further nine months (time for several more generations), after which he carried out a final analysis of male spot numbers. At 20 months, the populations had diverged even more than at the time of the second sample, with groups A and B now averaging 13.0 spots per fish and group C averaging 9.5 (Figure 10.3).

Do the results summarized in Figure 10.3 support the hypothesis that, through natural selection, the presence of predatory fish affects the number of spots on male guppies?

Yes, they do. Several guppy generations after the introduction of predators to some ponds, male guppies in those ponds that contained voracious predators had fewer spots than those in ponds that contained either no predators or predators that are innocuous to guppies.

Question 10.3   The purpose of the group C ponds was to see what the effect would be on the guppy populations of adding a voracious predator after several generations in which there had been no predation. What do you think was the purpose of the group A and B ponds? ◀

This example has illustrated four important points about natural selection. First, provided the three necessary and sufficient conditions listed in Section 10.1 are met, the form of a character can change from generation to generation. Second, the form of the character that results from natural selection represents a trade-off between the various ways in which that character affects the survival and reproduction of individuals. Third, natural selection can lead to a quite marked change in the form of a character in only a few generations. Finally, it shows that the theory of natural selection can be tested by carrying out experiments.

10.3 Other influences on evolution

One of the crucial conditions for natural selection to occur is that there must be variation. However, it is extremely important to appreciate that natural selection does not itself *cause* that variation; it simply acts on existing variation. The processes that do bring about variation are therefore major components of evolution. The most important of these processes, because it is really the ultimate source of all variation, is mutation. A **mutation** is an alteration in the genetic material which is copied from parent to offspring — the DNA in the cells of an organism (Section 3.1). Such an alteration may be associated with a change in the appearance or behaviour of an individual carrying it. For example, there might be a mutant male guppy that has no spots at all, or one that has an unusually large number of spots. We will return to the topic of mutation in Block 9, where we will also consider how sexual reproduction brings about further variation by 'shuffling' the chromosomes between generations.

Genetic drift is defined as chance variation in the genetic make-up of a *population* between one generation and the next. If, for a few years and purely by chance, the red-haired residents of Liverpool happened to have more children on average than the other residents did, then (as red hair is a heritable character) the proportion of red-haired people in the population of that city would increase. The change would be due to chance and not because red-haired people were better adapted than other people. Genetic drift would be responsible, not natural selection. In a large population, however, genetic drift is unlikely to have a great effect because chance differences in reproductive success between individuals will tend to even themselves out when a large number of individuals are involved. But in very small populations (say, fewer than 20 individuals) genetic drift can have a strong effect because if only one individual happens, purely by chance, to produce more offspring than the others, its characters will become more common in the next generation. Similarly, a particular character can easily disappear from a small population by genetic drift.

A somewhat different cause of variation between populations can be illustrated by the case of the Dunker sect. A number of small religious sects emigrated from Germany to the USA in the 18th century and have since married almost exclusively among their own numbers. The Dunkers are a sect that settled in Pennsylvania. The frequency of blood group A in the general population of Pennsylvania is 42%, and in Germany it is 45%. However, 60% of Dunkers are of blood group A.

How would you account for the unusually high frequency of blood group A among the Dunkers?

The small number of emigrants who established the Pennsylvania population in the 18th century must have included an unrepresentatively high number of people with blood group A.

For obvious reasons, this phenomenon is known as the **founder effect**. The frequency of a particular character in a particular population, in this case the frequency of blood group A in the Dunker population of Pennsylvania, may be due more to chance (the frequency of the character in the small founding population being different from that in the population from which it was derived) than to natural selection.

Activity 2.2 (continued)   Producing a glossary of biological terms

This section contains relatively few bold terms, so updating your glossary should be straightforward. In addition to these terms, you could consider entries in your glossary for Darwin's four propositions. ◀

10.4 Summary of Section 10

By biological evolution we mean that many of the organisms that inhabit the Earth today are different from those that inhabited it in the past.

Natural selection is one of several processes that can bring about evolution, although it can also promote stability rather than change. It follows that natural selection is not the same thing as evolution.

The four propositions underlying Darwin's theory of evolution through natural selection are: (1) more individuals are produced than can survive; (2) there is therefore a struggle for existence; (3) individuals within a species show variation; and (4) offspring tend to inherit their parents' characters.

The three necessary and sufficient conditions for natural selection to occur are: (1) a struggle for existence; (2) variation; and (3) inheritance.

Endler's experiment with guppies demonstrated that evolution through natural selection can occur in relatively few generations.

Mutation is the ultimate source of variation.

The frequency of a particular character in a particular population may be due to chance events (e.g. the founder effect and/or genetic drift) rather than to natural selection.

11 The evolution of clutch size in birds: a case study in natural selection

In this section, we look at how natural selection acts upon the variation that exists in natural populations to produce change in the characters of organisms over time. We do this by examining a single character in detail: clutch size in birds (i.e. the number of eggs produced in a single breeding episode).

For birds living in Britain, spring is the breeding season. In most species, individuals form pairs, one or both members of which build a nest, and then mate. The female lays a number of eggs in the nest, usually at intervals of one or two days, which one or both parents then incubate by sitting on them. Incubation provides the heat necessary for the embryos in the eggs to continue to develop. Although it may have taken the female many days to lay a complete clutch, in many species incubation does not begin until the last egg has been laid, which means that all the eggs hatch within a few hours of each other. In this section we are concerned with the point at which the female apparently 'decides' to stop laying and start incubating, hence determining the number of offspring she and her mate will attempt to rear.

What happens after the eggs hatch depends on the species and, in this context, there are two major categories. In ducks, geese, poultry, pheasants, partridges, etc. the young hatch at an advanced stage of development. They are led away from the nest very soon after hatching and typically are not fed by the parents.

⬤ From general knowledge, where do most of these species make their nests?

◯ They nest on the ground.

The ground is a risky place to be for a chick, which is much more likely to be seen by a predator than a well-camouflaged, immobile egg. It is therefore essential that chicks are soon ready to be led to a safer place, such as dense cover or open water, by one or both parents.

In species that typically nest in trees or burrows, the young are blind and helpless at hatching. They remain in the nest for several days or weeks, wholly dependent on food brought to them by their parents. Such familiar garden species as blackbirds, thrushes, tits and robins behave in this way.

11.1 Variation and clutch size

There is enormous variation in clutch size in birds. For example, gannets (*Sula bassana*) generally lay only one egg, but occasionally two; lapwings (*Vanellus vanellus*) usually lay 4; great tits (*Parus major*) have a clutch size that varies between 5 and 11, blue tits (*P. caeruleus*) between 7 and 14; grey partridges (*Perdix perdix*) may lay anything between 9 and 20. These figures illustrate that clutch size not only varies between species, but can also vary considerably *within* a species. This variation among individuals within a species is one reason why clutch size is a very good character in which to study the effects of natural selection.

Some of the variation in clutch size that occurs within a species is inherited; individuals that lay large clutches tend to be from large clutches themselves. It is estimated that in great tits about 40% of the variation in clutch size is due to inheritance. The rest of the variation can be explained in terms of particular environmental factors. For example, in many species clutch size varies with latitude and therefore climate, day length, etc. In the robin (*Erithacus rubecula*), mean clutch size is 6.3 in Scandinavia, 5.9 in central France, 4.9 in Spain, 4.2 in North Africa, and 3.5 in the Canary Islands. However, even within a locality, there is considerable within-species variation in clutch size (Figure 11.1). Some of this variation can be attributed to variation between years. In many species, mean clutch size for a population varies from one year to the next, for reasons that will become apparent shortly. There remains, however, a lot of variation that is due to other factors. Let us consider some of the factors that might limit clutch size in any particular species of bird.

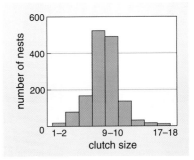

Figure 11.1 Clutch size in a population of great tits living in Wytham Wood near Oxford, from data collected over many years. Clutch sizes range from 1–2 (bar on far left) to 17–18 (far right).

Food supply during egg-laying

Eggs are energy- and nutrient-rich entities and a female has to eat a lot of food to produce a clutch. In a small bird like a blue tit, the mass of a female's completed clutch far exceeds her own body mass. Clutch size may, therefore, be limited by the amount of food available during the period of egg-laying. In fact, from numerous studies of this possibility, it appears that in only a few species is clutch size limited in this way.

Incubation

For eggs to develop properly, they must be kept at the right temperature. In a cold climate, heat is provided by a parent's body. If an individual lays too large a clutch, one or more eggs will, at any one time, be exposed and chilled, disrupting their development. Thus, there is an upper limit on the number of eggs that birds can incubate.

Food supply after hatching

Following hatching, the chicks of many bird species must be fed by their parents until their feathers are fully developed (i.e. the chicks fledge), enabling them to fly and become independent of their parents. Because chicks are growing, their food requirements are very high and one or both parents must devote virtually all their time to foraging for food to bring back to the chicks (Section 7). The larger the clutch, the more onerous is this parental burden. An individual that attempts to rear too many chicks may fail to rear any if it cannot provide sufficient food. As we shall see, this is much the most important limitation on clutch size in the majority of birds.

Before we go further in this discussion of clutch size, it is necessary to return to the concept of a trade-off. Consider the following two statements which, in general, are true for birds:

(a) The larger the clutch an individual female lays, the more nestlings she will have.

(b) Within a clutch, larger eggs produce larger nestlings, and larger nestlings are more likely to fledge than smaller ones.

Question 11.1   What trade-off, arising from (a) and (b) above, might influence an individual female's clutch size? ◀

The answer to Question 11.1 described just one important trade-off that influences the evolution of clutch size; there are others, one of which we will encounter later on.

11.2 An hypothesis about the evolution of clutch size

Science involves the formulation and testing of hypotheses and so, before we go further, we need a testable hypothesis about the evolution of clutch size in birds. The Oxford zoologist David Lack proposed the first such hypothesis which was based on the theory of natural selection. Lack argued that, for each species, *natural selection favours the clutch size that results in the most offspring surviving to maturity*. This is a very simple and apparently reasonable hypothesis, but it has no value if it cannot be tested. Since Lack proposed the hypothesis, it has been extensively tested by experiment and by observation.

Experimental test of Lack's hypothesis

Clutch size can be manipulated by removing eggs from the clutches of some birds and adding them to the clutches of others. If Lack's hypothesis is correct, both reduced and enlarged clutches should yield fewer surviving progeny than clutches that are left at their original size. Just such manipulations were carried out by H. G. Smith and co-workers in Sweden between 1983 and 1987. They manipulated the sizes of 221 great tit clutches which originally contained 8–9 eggs, so that reduced clutches contained 4–5 eggs, enlarged clutches 13–14 eggs and undisturbed clutches were left with 8–9 eggs. They then monitored, first, the number of chicks that fledged from each nest and, second, the number of those fledglings that survived to the next spring.

On average, a larger number of surviving offspring were produced from original, undisturbed clutches than from enlarged clutches. However, the survival rate of nestlings from reduced clutches was higher than that from original clutches. Despite this, undisturbed clutches produced the highest overall number of offspring surviving to the next spring. A strong clue as to why this occurred is provided by measurements that the researchers took of nestlings just before they fledged. Chicks from larger clutches were lighter and smaller than chicks from other clutches. Thus, many chicks from enlarged clutches did not get enough food to grow to a sufficient size to survive their first winter. Chicks from reduced clutches were large enough, but there were not enough of them for such clutches to be more productive than undisturbed clutches. These results show that tits lay a clutch whose size is optimum for them and so support Lack's hypothesis in that the size of clutch they actually lay is their most productive.

- Why is that last statement not the same as saying that a clutch size of 8–9 is the most productive?

- Because great tits can lay clutches bigger than 8–9 eggs and such clutches may be more productive. (Remember, the experiment only tested tits that had laid 8–9 eggs.)

So, what is the most productive clutch size? This question has been answered using the second technique.

Observational test of Lack's hypothesis

It is possible, by carrying out intensive and laborious fieldwork, to document both the sizes of a large number of clutches and the number of mature progeny that result from those clutches. Researchers can then see whether the clutches that most birds produce are of the size that yields the most surviving offspring. Wytham Wood, on the outskirts of Oxford, is a largely oak woodland in which the great tit population has been intensively studied since 1947.

From Figure 11.1, what is the size of clutch laid most frequently by great tits?

The most frequent clutch size laid by great tits is 7–8.

However, the most productive clutch size, in terms of the number of young birds surviving to the following year, was 12.

Question 11.2 Does this disparity between the most frequent clutch size and the most productive clutch size support Lack's hypothesis? ◀

How can we explain this disparity? Does it mean that natural selection does not influence the clutch size of great tits, or that Lack's hypothesis is wrong, or that there are additional factors that have to be taken into account? The answer is that Lack was correct in principle, but that the situation is more complex than he envisaged. We will now look at an additional factor that influences the evolution of clutch size.

11.3 The cost of reproduction

Figure 11.2 shows data for the lifespan of female and male great tits in the Wytham population.

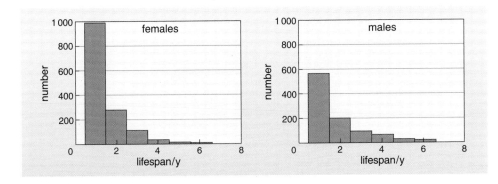

Figure 11.2 Lifespans of female and male great tits living in Wytham Wood near Oxford, from data collected over many years.

When do most great tits die?

Within their first year, an effect that is more marked in females than in males.

The greatest mortality among great tits occurs at the onset of winter, when the majority of young birds that fledged in the spring of that year, and many adult birds, die of starvation. A proportion of the population does, however, survive for more than one year and consequently has more than one opportunity to breed. Great tits are thus iteroparous animals, a fact that introduces another trade-off that must be considered. In any organism that breeds more than once, there is a trade-off between energy expended in a current breeding episode and the probability of surviving to the next one and hence breeding again. An individual that 'puts its all' into its current breeding effort may produce many offspring, but be left so weak and undernourished that it does not survive to breed again. Data that illustrate this effect in a close relative of the great tit, the blue tit, are shown in Figure 11.3.

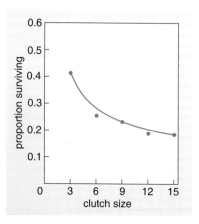

Figure 11.3 The proportion of adult female blue tits surviving to the year after breeding plotted against experimentally manipulated clutch size.

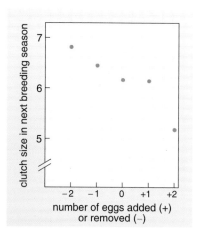

Figure 11.4 Mean clutch size of female collared flycatchers in the breeding season after that in which eggs were either added to or removed from their nests.

Do the data shown in Figure 11.3 support the hypothesis that there is a trade-off between current breeding effort and survival?

Yes, they do. Individuals that have smaller clutches in one year are more likely to survive to the next year.

The hypothesis that there is a trade-off between current breeding effort and long-term survival, and thus future reproduction, has been experimentally tested in another bird species, the collared flycatcher (*Ficedula albicollis*). Clutch sizes were altered by adding or subtracting one or two eggs from the clutches of several pairs of birds, and then recording the clutch size of the same pairs in the next breeding season. The results are shown in Figure 11.4.

Question 11.3   Do these data support the hypothesis that there is a trade-off between current and future reproduction? ◄

The recognition that there is a cost of reproduction, and that there is therefore a trade-off between present and future reproduction, enables us to modify Lack's hypothesis, so that the modified hypothesis says: *natural selection favours the clutch size that results in the most offspring surviving to maturity over the whole of an individual's lifetime.*

The disparity between what seems to be the most productive clutch size for great tits and their most common clutch size can now be at least partially explained. The optimum clutch size for great tits in a given year is less than the most productive clutch size, because a smaller clutch increases the probability of an individual surviving to have another clutch in the following year.

Detailed analyses of the Wytham great tit data do not, however, suggest that this is the end of the story. There remains a lot of unexplained variation in clutch size. Other factors which influence clutch size include:

- Variation between years in the weather and food supply: such variation means that some clutch sizes are favoured in one year, other clutch sizes in another year.
- Variation in great tit density: birds living in areas in which there is a high density of great tits tend to produce smaller clutches, as do those living in areas in which oak trees are scarce.
- Variation in the age of the population: young birds, breeding for the first time, lay smaller clutches than older, experienced birds.

All these effects suggest that, somehow, individual great tits are able to adjust their clutch size according to the immediate circumstances in which they find themselves.

11.4 Variation in clutch size among bird species

Great tits are but one bird species among many. What appears to determine clutch size in one species is not always true of other species. For example, although providing supplementary food increases fledging success in kestrels (*Falco tinnunculus*) as might be predicted, it has no impact on the fledging success of lesser black-backed gulls (*Larus fuscus*).

Laying a clutch of eggs of an optimum size can be regarded as a solution to a problem, that of matching the effort an individual puts into producing and rearing young with the food supply available to feed those young. An intriguing aspect of the behaviour of great tits and other birds is that, in laying a clutch of a certain size, they are, in essence, anticipating how much food will be available at a later stage in the breeding season. Some birds have evolved a quite different solution to this problem. Many birds of prey (particularly the larger ones, such as eagles), and also egrets, start incubating their clutch as soon as the first egg is laid. This means that the development of the resulting chicks is staggered, because the eggs hatch at intervals, as many days apart as they were laid. The oldest, most developed, chick can always dominate its siblings and be the first to get any food brought to the nest by the parents; even in years of poor food supply, the first chick usually gets enough to eat. The later chicks get enough food to survive only in years of good supply; in poor years, they typically die of starvation. In this way the brood size of such birds is matched, through competition among unequal chicks, to the available food supply.

A final point that emerges from the many studies that have been made of clutch size in birds concerns the rate at which natural selection brings about evolutionary change. Many of the birds that currently breed in northern temperate regions such as Britain did not do so 5 000 years ago, yet now they appear to have evolved so that their clutch sizes are characteristic of where they breed (recall the robin, mentioned in Section 11.1). From measurements of the breeding success of individuals laying different-sized clutches in species such as the great tit, it has been calculated that natural selection can lead to a change of 1.5 eggs per clutch in as little as ten years. For many species of birds, therefore, clutch size is not static over evolutionary time but is a dynamic character, capable of rapid changes if environmental conditions alter. The climate of Britain is currently changing quite fast (Block 2) and we can anticipate that the clutch size of many birds will evolve with these changes.

11.5 Fitness

Biologists often use familiar words in special and unfamiliar ways. One such word is 'fitness', a very important concept in the study of natural selection. In everyday language, fitness is something we acquire by taking exercise; in biology, it is a measure of an individual organism's biological *success*.

○ Recall from Section 6 what it means to say that an individual organism is 'successful'.

○ A successful individual is one that leaves many descendants.

To say that fitness is a *measure* of individual success means that it is not just an abstract concept but something to which we can assign a specific numerical value. Here we will first explore the meaning and definition of fitness and then, again using the example of clutch size in birds, show how it can be measured in nature.

The second part of Darwin's third premise says that 'Those [individuals] with advantageous characters have a greater probability of survival, and therefore of reproducing, in the struggle for existence' (Section 10.1). The concept of fitness relates to the 'greater probability' referred to in this sentence. Individuals certainly vary in their probabilities of survival. Although Darwin emphasized the importance of variation in those characters that enhance survival, he also recognized that, for such variations to evolve, they must be passed on in reproduction. The modern view of fitness emphasizes the reproductive success of individuals, defined as the number of an individual's progeny that survive to adulthood, relative to that of other individuals. However, an individual might produce many offspring that survive to reproductive age but which themselves fail to reproduce, perhaps because they are less robust than other individuals or because they are the sterile progeny of a hybrid mating (Section 4). The full definition of fitness therefore incorporates the reproductive success of the progeny:

> **Fitness** is defined as the *relative* ability of an organism to survive and leave offspring that themselves survive and leave offspring.

This definition is simple and concise, but it is not a convenient one for an evolutionary biologist who seeks to measure fitness in a natural population. Suppose, for example, that you wanted to measure fitness in a population of great tits. It is obvious that you would have to record the fledging success of many pairs of great tits, not just for one year, but for up to six years, as some tits live that long (Figure 11.2). You would also have to follow the survival and breeding success of all those birds' progeny, some of which might also live for six years. Thus, to measure accurately the fitness of a single cohort of great tits (i.e. all the birds born in a given year) would take something like 13 years. A succession of biologists in Oxford have effectively done this over 50 years. However, some tortoises live for 100 or more years and, whereas great tits lay easily-counted numbers of eggs in convenient nest boxes, some fishes shed millions of eggs into the ocean. Accurate measurements of fitness for such animals are clearly impossible.

Because it is often so difficult to measure fitness accurately, in most studies of animals and plants, researchers measure one or more **components of fitness**. Examples include survival to reproductive age, number of fertilized eggs produced, number of surviving young, etc. What these components have in common is that they are to some extent inherited. The ability of an individual to lay a large clutch or produce offspring that survive is partly determined by what that individual inherits from its parents. Many other factors affect the survival of offspring (e.g. the abundance of predators) but, because these other factors are not inherited, they are not components of fitness.

There is one final, but extremely important, point about fitness in the context of natural selection. What matters is not the actual value of an individual's fitness in terms of the number of its progeny that survive to reproduce, but which individuals have *higher* fitness than others. Fitness is thus a *relative* measure, with the most fit individual in a population being assigned the value 1. All other individuals have their fitness expressed as fractions or proportions of 1. Thus, if the fittest bird in a population of great tits leaves ten offspring that survive to reproduce, a bird that leaves five has a fitness of $\dfrac{5}{10} \times 1 = 0.5$.

Activity 11.1   Estimating fitness from life history data

In this activity you will analyse data for great tits to reinforce your understanding of the concept of fitness. ◀

Activity 11.1 should have served to illustrate two points about the measurement of fitness:

1   Components of fitness, such as clutch size in a single year, can be very poor indicators of overall fitness. Even survival is quite a poor indicator of fitness.

2   Accurate estimates of fitness require the collection of data for many components of fitness. The more such measures we have, the more accurate our final estimate of fitness is likely to be.

The data in Activity 11.1 also reinforce a point about natural selection that was emphasized earlier, that fitness results from trade-offs during an individual's life. In this instance, we can see for bird 4 how reproduction in the first year is traded-off against survival. She had the smallest clutch size in year 1, but survived for three years and ended up with the highest fitness.

Question 11.4   On the basis of the data in Activity 11.1 and your analysis of these data, which characters do you think will be favoured by natural selection acting on great tits? ◀

Animals and plants are constantly exposed to a diversity of hazards and challenging situations that threaten their continued survival and their reproductive success. Natural selection is going on all the time. We can, however, identify certain factors that cause mortality or reduce reproductive success at specific times or in specific contexts. These are called *episodes of selection*. For example, survival during the first winter of life is an important episode of selection for great tits, one which eliminates the great majority of each generation. Clutch size and survival of fledglings are also distinct episodes of selection. In a year when the weather is bad, mortality among nestlings may be very high, making that episode of selection very severe. Fitness is the outcome of many episodes of selection, some quite weak, others much more severe, in their effects.

Activity 11.2   Explaining the concept of a trade-off

In this activity you will need to recall a number of factors that influence clutch size and use one of those factors to explain the principle of trade-off. ◀

11.6 Evolution and natural selection

For Darwin, natural selection was a theory that sought to explain how living species have evolved from ancestral species. It was thus essentially a theory about the history of life. In this context, natural selection can provide a plausible explanation of the evolutionary history of living organisms, but such explanations cannot be framed in terms of scientific hypotheses that can be tested. It is not possible to run an 'action replay' of past evolution, to test whether hypotheses about evolution in the past are correct.

For contemporary biologists, the theory of natural selection provides a framework for what is happening to organisms in the present. In this context, it can be used to formulate hypotheses that can be tested by collecting observational and experimental data. The examples of the guppy (Section 10.2) and clutch size in birds illustrate this approach.

From reading about these studies, you should appreciate that natural selection is not something that happened only in the past. Rather, it is a process that is continually acting on the characters of living organisms.

11.7 Summary of Section 11

Clutch size in birds illustrates the general principle that, for any character, there is a trade-off between the costs and benefits that character confers on an individual.

For an individual bird, clutch size involves trade-offs between egg size and clutch size, and between current clutch size and long-term survival.

Lack's hypothesis, that natural selection favours the clutch size that results in the most offspring surviving to maturity, was tested by collecting field data on clutch size and by carrying out simple experiments in which clutch size was manipulated.

Lack's original hypothesis has been modified to take into account the cost of reproduction; a bird's lifetime reproductive success can be maximized if it lays a smaller clutch than that which maximizes its reproductive success in the current season.

Clutch size is a dynamic character which, under the influence of natural selection, is continually changing in response to varying environmental conditions.

Fitness is a numerical measure of the *relative* reproductive success of individuals of the same species. Fitness can rarely, if ever, be measured with absolute completeness and accuracy; it is therefore usually estimated by collecting data on several components of fitness.

Levels of explanation in biology

A clutch of birds' eggs represents many things simultaneously. Most obviously, it represents the progeny of a pair of adults and can therefore be considered an investment of time and effort by the adults. The clutch is also part of the population of a particular species; the size of the clutch, and the parents' success or otherwise in raising it, therefore influences the size of the population in future. The clutch is also part of several food chains; it is a potential resource for other organisms (e.g. weasels and parasites), as well as being a potential consumer of resources (e.g. caterpillars) itself.

These are just three of many different ways of looking at a clutch of birds' eggs — three different perspectives on the clutch.

 What other perspectives can you think of?

You might have thought of the perspective of development, the fact that each egg contains an embryo which will develop into an adult bird if it survives. Another perspective is that of metabolism, the process that enables a developing chick to convert egg yolk into body material and to release the energy it requires for growth, movement, etc.

These different perspectives on a clutch of eggs are called **levels of explanation**. They are levels only in the sense that 'higher' levels contain or encompass 'lower' levels. Thus, the relatively 'high' level of ecology contains information about the populations of different species within an ecosystem; the level of population of a particular species contains information about individual organisms within the population; the level of the individual organism contains information about its metabolism, etc. It is very important to realize that there is no sense in which one level provides a better, or more comprehensive, explanation than another. Each level simply provides a different explanation of, or if you prefer, a different perspective on, the biological phenomenon in question.

A characteristic of biology as a science is that, while attention is often focused on one particular level of explanation, it is seldom possible to ignore entirely the levels of explanation immediately 'above' and 'below'. For example, a biologist studying annual fluctuations in the size of the sparrowhawk population in an area must bear in mind both how the sparrowhawk fits into the food web of which it is a part and also the metabolic requirements of individual birds within the population.

The process of taking the living world apart in this block has largely been concerned with levels of explanation from the individual organism 'upwards', i.e. families, populations, ecosystems. It has touched on levels of explanation 'below' that of the individual (e.g. metabolism, cells) only to the extent necessary for other levels to make sense. Later in the course, Block 9 will fill in much of this missing detail, when an understanding of metabolism and inheritance at the molecular level allows us to 'put the living world together', and understand the behaviour of organisms and populations much better.

Activity 12.1   Reviewing your study of Block 4: using scientific language

In this activity you will review the techniques you have developed for learning scientific terms and using them correctly. ◀

Questions: answers and comments

Comments on the answers are given in curly brackets {...}.

Question 2.1   Duration of the life cycle and generation time are the same thing. The duration of the human life cycle/generation time is about 15 years. Since people can live about 80 years, the difference between the length of human life and the length of the life cycle/generation time is about 65 years. {This is in marked contrast with many other species; at the other extreme is the Atlantic salmon (*Salmo salar*), which dies immediately after it reproduces at the age of about seven years, i.e. there is no difference between the duration of its life cycle/ generation time and the length of its life.}

Question 2.2   You may have thought of two or three answers to this question. First, not all parts of a plant are exposed to the Sun. The roots, and those parts of the tree underneath the bark, receive no direct sunlight. So these unexposed parts have to rely on respiration for energy. Second, plants capture solar energy by photosynthesis and photosynthesis produces sugars, from which other organic molecules are subsequently made. Solar energy therefore cannot be used directly to 'drive' any other parts of metabolism directly. Once the energy has been stored in organic molecules, respiration is needed to release it for use in metabolism. Third, photosynthesis cannot occur in the dark. Respiration enables plants to have a source of energy at night.

Question 2.3   (a) Yes, the adult mayfly metabolizes. In order to be active, an organism must obtain energy from organic molecules by respiration.

(b) Organisms have to grow at some stage in their life cycle, but not at every stage. The mayfly grew when it was young but does not need to grow as an adult.

(c) The mayfly is a heterotroph, although it feeds only when young. The mayfly is an animal and all animals are heterotrophs.

(d) There are many possibilities, including: most adult insects (e.g. flies, bees, wasps, ants), fungal spores, plant seeds, dried yeast, etc. Don't forget you and me, of course.

Question 2.4   It doesn't matter whether you put the bread in a dark cupboard or leave it on a table in the light. Fungi are heterotrophs so they grow just as well with or without light. {Do feel free to try this experiment if you would like to confirm the result for yourself.}

Question 2.5   (a) The stages through which an organism passes until reproduction are known as its *life cycle* (8).

(b) The manufacture of sugars from carbon dioxide and water is *photosynthesis* (5).

(c) The chemical transformations characteristic of living organisms are collectively known as *metabolism* (3).

(d) The release of energy from organic molecules occurs in *respiration* (4).

Question 2.6   Autotrophs can metabolize (3), respire (4), photosynthesize (5), reproduce (7) and have a life cycle (8). Heterotrophs can metabolize (3), respire (4), reproduce (7) and have a life cycle (8).

Question 2.7   Metabolism in fungal spores must mean respiration is taking place (fungi are heterotrophs so they do not photosynthesize). Respiration is described by the chemical reaction:

organic carbon + oxygen → carbon dioxide + water   (2.2)

To prove that respiration was occurring, it would be necessary to measure changes in one of these four items. There would be a reduction in organic carbon and oxygen and an increase in carbon dioxide and water. You have not been provided with any information to decide between these four, but it is generally easier to measure carbon dioxide production or oxygen removal.

Question 3.1   (a) Sugars require assistance to move across the cell membrane.

(b) Other molecules move across the cell membrane by diffusion.

Question 3.2   The wrong statement is (d). Prokaryotes do contain genetic material (DNA), but it is not contained in a nucleus.

Question 3.3   (a) (iv) Each DNA molecule forms one chromosone, so there are exactly the same number of chromosomes as there are molecules of DNA during growth phase I.

(b) (iv) The length of a DNA molecule is exactly the same during cell division as during interphase. {The DNA is coiled in mitosis, but the overall length of the molecule is the same.}

Question 3.4 You would expect to see 92 chromosomes. The 46 chromosomes replicate to make 92 chromatids prior to mitosis. These 92 chromatids separate at anaphase to become 92 individual chromosomes. The cell has not yet divided so there are 92 chromosomes in the cell at anaphase.

Question 3.5 (a) In a diploid cell, each autosome is one of a pair (and this is sometimes true also for the sex chromosomes). However, there may be *many* pairs of chromosomes in a cell. In a human cell there are either 22 or 23 pairs of chromosomes. {Also, a few eukaryotic cells — for example human red blood cells — do not possess any chromosomes when mature.}

(b) This is only true after chromosomes have replicated themselves during interphase and before the chromatid pairs separate to become independent chromosomes at the start of anaphase.

(c) No chromosome has its own nucleus. Each nucleus may contain many chromosomes.

(d) Interphase begins when cell division ends and finishes as mitosis starts (Figure 3.5).

(e) The cell could be eukaryotic, since a eukaryotic cell has no nucleus during mitosis. {Mature red blood cells have no nuclei at all.}

Question 4.1 The first character is source of food: almost all plants are autotrophs (i.e. they make their own food by photosynthesis), while all fungi and animals are heterotrophs. The second is mobility: most animals have the ability to move in search of food, while fungi and plants do not.

{The expression 'fairly reliably' had to be used in the question because, as so often in biology, there are exceptions. A few plant species have lost (or reduced) their ability to feed autotrophically and so live heterotrophically, feeding on other plants either while they are alive (i.e. as parasites) or after their death (i.e. as saprophytes). Insectivorous plants (e.g. Venus's flytrap) are autotrophs that derive *some* of their nutrients from insects they trap. Some animals are not mobile (at least as adults) and rely on food being brought to them in water currents, etc.}

Question 4.2 Figure 4.10 shows how *C. familiaris* can be 'nested' within successively broader, more inclusive, levels of classification.

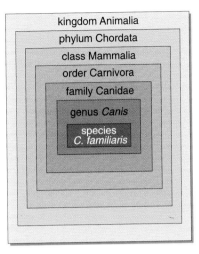

Figure 4.10 Diagram to show how *C. familiaris* can be 'nested' within successively broader levels of classification.

Question 5.1 Since 63% of the Indonesian bug species were new to science, 37% had previously been described. If we assume that the 82 000 species which have been described world-wide (Box 5.1) represent 37% of the total, then 1% of the total would be 82 000/37 and 100% of the total would be (82 000/37) × 100, which is about 220 000. This suggests that the world-wide total is about a quarter of a million (2.5×10^5) bug species. {This estimate depends on there being the same percentage of previously unknown bug species everywhere in the world. This is unlikely to be the case, so the estimate needs to be treated with caution.}

Question 5.2 Among Erwin's assumptions are the following: (1) that all the arthropods in the crowns of the trees would be collected using the insecticide-fog method; (2) that the tree in which 163 species of beetle were found was typical of tropical trees in general; (3) that beetles represent 40% of arthropod species (the Box 5.1 data suggest 33%); (4) that there are about 5×10^4 species of tropical tree world-wide; (5) that most arthropod species are confined to a single tree species; and (6) that half as many arthropod species live on the ground as in the crowns of tropical trees.

{This was not an easy question, so don't be disheartened if you didn't think of all the above assumptions.}

Question 6.1 (a) The main consequence of asexual reproduction is that the DNA of any offspring produced is identical to that of its parent, i.e. the offspring is a clone of the parent.

(b) Its parent was biologically successful (i.e. it produced at least one offspring). The asexually produced offspring (or clone) contains exactly the same DNA as its parent. You would therefore expect the clone of a successful organism also to be successful.

Question 6.2   (a) A male *spermatozoon* fertilizes a female *ovum* to produce a *diploid zygote*.

(b) Gametes are *haploid* and are produced by cell division which involves *meiosis*.

Question 6.3   (a) A zygote is defined as the cell that results from a spermatozoon fertilizing an ovum. Since asexual reproduction does not involve sperm, ova or fertilization, there is no zygote in asexual reproduction. {Hence Dolly's first cell being described as 'the equivalent of a zygote' (Box 6.1).}

(b) A spermatozoon contributes only half of the zygote's chromosomes. The other half come from the female. Thus, the zygote is not a clone of the male contributing the spermatozoon. {And neither is it a clone of the female contributing the ovum.}

Question 8.1   (a) The sheep population in Tasmania increased steadily from about 1820 to around 1850; thereafter it remained fairly stable, with small, irregular fluctuations from year to year.

(b) Water fleas in an aquarium fluctuate in numbers, reaching a peak every 40 days. Between the peaks, the number falls to very low values.

(c) The populations of all three whale species have shown a general decline (from the 1940s for the blue whale, from the 1950s for the fin whale and from the 1960s for the sei whale).

Question 8.2   (e), (g), (h) (i) and (j). The population of a bird species would tend to increase if individuals lived a long time (i.e. there was low annual mortality (g) and high longevity (i)), reproduced repeatedly (i.e. there was iteroparity (e)) and at high frequency (j), and clutch sizes were large (h).

Question 8.3   The short answer is because of trade-offs. A bird that produces large clutches (h) cannot reproduce frequently (j) because production of each clutch requires a lot of resources. Also, large clutches require more looking after because in due course there are more mouths to feed. Large clutches are therefore likely to suffer higher mortality than small clutches while the adults are absent from the nest.

Question 8.4   (a) The statement is incorrect. An organism can indeed display both high r and low r, though not at the same time (e.g. *Hydra*).

(b) The statement is incorrect. On the evidence given in Section 8, fishes and frogs are both high r, low K organisms. {However, there are exceptions, e.g. the strawberry frog (Figure 2.6).}

(c) The statement is correct, since the species has not been specified. It follows that 'the population of the North Sea' cannot be estimated.

Question 8.5   See Figure 8.6.

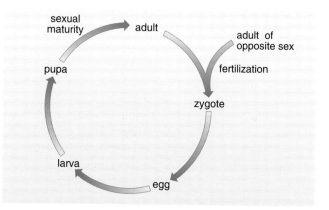

Figure 8.6   Life cycle of the holly leaf miner (*Phytomyza ilicis*).

Question 10.1   Two: one that 'replaces' her in the population when she dies and one that 'replaces' one of the males with whom she has mated during her life. If any more than two survive on average, then the population would increase.

Question 10.2   Bright coloration makes male guppies more conspicuous to predators. Thus, where predators are present, it will be the less colourful males that tend to survive and reproduce. Putting it another way, in streams where predators are present, males have evolved less bright coloration, an adaptation that reduces their risk of being eaten.

Question 10.3   The purpose of the group A ponds was to show what happened over the same period of time in the absence of predators. The change in the number of spots in the group C guppies might have taken place anyway, whether or not the predators had been introduced. The group A ponds allowed Endler to check on this possibility. {The group A ponds therefore served as 'controls' for the 'experimental' group C ponds. A 'control' is an important feature of scientific experimental procedure. It enables the investigator to be sure that any change taking place in the 'experimental' set-up is due to the factor that has been experimentally changed, and not to some other factor which has not been accounted for.}

The group B ponds allowed Endler to check whether any change observed in the group C ponds could have been due, not so much to the addition of a fish that preys on guppies, but to the addition of *any* other species of fish or even *any* other species of predatory fish (whether it preyed on guppies or not). {So again, the group B ponds served as 'controls' for the 'experimental' group C ponds.}

Question 11.1 There is a trade-off between egg size and clutch size. A few very large eggs might reliably produce a few fledglings; many very small eggs will possibly produce none. However, an intermediate number of intermediate-sized eggs may well produce more fledglings than either extreme. In other words, there is an optimum clutch size and an optimum egg size which together produce the greatest number of fledglings. {The optimum values of clutch size and egg size will depend on environmental conditions, such as temperature and rainfall, because these will affect food supply and nestling survival.}

Question 11.2 No, it does not. It suggests that, on average, great tits lay fewer eggs than would be expected if natural selection favoured the most productive clutch size.

Question 11.3 Yes, they do. Females that had eggs removed from their nests had larger clutches in the following season than both those whose clutches were unchanged and those whose clutches were increased in size.

Question 11.4 Birds that don't survive their first winter have a fitness of 0! There is therefore strong selective pressure on those characters which would enable a young bird to survive their first winter {such as growth rate (to be big enough) and feather condition (to be warm enough and to fly strongly)}. Birds that have produced clutches of modest size in year 1 tend to survive better and ultimately have higher fitness. Selection in great tits therefore favours small clutch size and iteroparity, over large clutch size and semelparity.

Acknowledgements

Grateful acknowledgement is made to the following sources for permission to reproduce material in this block:

Figures

Figures 2.2 and 4.3c: Ardea, London; *Figure 2.3*: Roger Viollet, Paris; *Figures 2.6 and 2.8*: Oxford Scientific Films; *Figures 2.9, 4.2a and b, 4.3a and b, 5.2, 6.2, 6.3 and 10.2*: Heather Angel, Biofotos; *Figures 3.6, 4.7a and b*: Biophoto Associates; *Figure 4.1*: Frank Lane Picture Agency, Images of Nature; *Figure 4.6*: Science Photo Library; *Figure 5.1*: Council of the Linnean Society/Todd-White & Sons; *Figure 5.2*: Courtesy of Chris Wilson; *Figure 8.1*: Begon, M., Harper, J. L. and Townsend, C. R. 1986, *Ecology*, Blackwell Science Ltd; *Figure 8.5*: Courtesy of Marion Hall; *Figure 10.1*: English Heritage Photo Library; *Figure 10.3*: Endler, J. A. 1980, 'Natural selection on colour patterns in *Poecilia reticulata*', *Evolution*, **34**(1), pp. 76–91, Allen Press, Inc.; *Figures 11.1 and 11.2*: McCleery, R. H. and Perrins, C. M. 'Lifetime reproductive success of the Great Tit, *Parus major*' in Clutton-Brock, T. H. (ed.) 1988, *Reproductive Success*: *Studies of individual variation in contrasting breeding systems*, © 1988 by The University of Chicago Press Ltd; *Figure 11.3*: Sibly, R. M. and Calow, P. 1986, *Physiological Ecology of Animals*: *An evolutionary approach*, Blackwell Scientific Publications; *Figure 11.4*: Gustafsson, L. and Sutherland, W. J. 1988, 'The costs of reproduction in the collared flycatcher *Ficedula albicollis*', *Nature*, **335**, pp. 813–815, Macmillan Magazines Ltd.

Photos on title page

Ardea, London.

Index

Entries and page numbers in **bold type** refer to key words which are printed in **bold** in the text and which are defined in the Glossary. These are terms that we expect you to be able to explain the meaning of, and use correctly, both during and at the end of the course. An entry followed by G indicates a term which is defined in the Glossary but which is not bold in the text. Where the page number is given in *italics*, the indexed information is carried mainly or wholly in an illustration or table. Section summaries and answers to questions are not indexed.